THE INCREDIBLE DIARY OF...

Adventures From Lancashire

Edited By Megan Roberts

First published in Great Britain in 2019 by:

Young Writers
Remus House
Coltsfoot Drive
Peterborough
PE2 9BF
Telephone: 01733 890066
Website: www.youngwriters.co.uk

Book Design by Ashley Janson
© Copyright Contributors 2019
Softback ISBN 978-1-78988-666-5
Hardback ISBN 978-1-78988-972-7
Printed and bound in the UK by BookPrintingUK
Website: www.bookprintinguk.com
YB0411F

Foreword

Dear Reader,

You will never guess what I did today! Shall I tell you? Some primary school pupils wrote some diary entries and I got to read them, and they were **EXCELLENT!**

They wrote them in school and sent them to us here at Young Writers. We'd given their teachers some bright and funky worksheets to fill in, and some fun and fabulous (and free) resources to help spark ideas and get inspiration flowing.

And it clearly worked because **WOW!!** I can't believe the adventures I've been reading about. Real people, make-believe people, dogs and unicorns, even objects like pencils all feature and these diaries all have one thing in common – they are **JAM-PACKED** with imagination!

We live and breathe creativity here at Young Writers – it gives us life! We want to pass our love of the written word onto the next generation and what better way to do that than to celebrate their writing by publishing it in a book!

It sets their work free from homework books and notepads and puts it where it deserves to be – **OUT IN THE WORLD!** Each awesome author in this book should be **super proud** of themselves, and now they've got proof of their imagination, their ideas and their creativity in black and white, to look back on in years to come!

Now that I've read all these diaries, I've somehow got to pick some winners! Oh my gosh it's going to be difficult to choose, but I'm going to have **SO MUCH FUN** doing it!

Bye!

Megan

Contents

Bolton Parish Church CE Primary School, Bolton

Raisa Ahmed (9)	1
Wasim Iftakhar (9)	2
Abbas Bin Usman (9)	4
Musa Baig (8)	6
Lilah Cameron (9)	8
Hashim Abbas (9)	9
Dior Destiny Boardman (9)	10
Ahmad Shahid (8)	11
Lawson Parkinson (8)	12

Gisburn Road Community Primary School, Barnoldswick

Harris Brierley (11)	13
Brett Harper (11)	14
Jamie Pearson (11)	16
Lia-J Lawson (10)	18
Alfie Holman (10)	20
Lily Rogan (11)	22
Mahek Noor Mahmood (10)	24
Isabelle Jesson (10)	26

Lever House Primary School, Farington

Daisy Walsh (9)	27
Joseph Rogers (9)	28
Erin Cadence Gibbons (8)	30
Isabel Pearson (10)	32
Isabella Blackburn (10)	34
Emily Joan Mamwell-Holme (9)	36
Octavia Mae Nicholson-Blezard (10)	38
Imogen Winters (8)	40

Sofia Alexa Higgins (7)	42
Hannah Grace Dobson (9)	44
May Hardy (10)	46
Abigail Doran (10)	48
Maisy Thornley (10)	50
Isaac Travers (8)	52
Joshua Privett (9)	54
Grace Langley (7)	56
Harry Thomas French (8)	58
Nicholas Christopher Morley (10)	60
Harry Walker (9)	62
Thomas Harry Masterson (8)	64
Megan Mahoney (10)	65
Thomas Sheehan (8)	66
Lucas Whish (8)	67
Madeline Briers (9)	68
Ehren Munday (8)	69
Aaron Holland (8)	70
Paige Hardiman (8)	71
Sofia Elizabeth Morley (8)	72

Queen Elizabeth's Grammar School, Blackburn

Eham Zaman (10)	73
Umar Karolia (9)	74
Fizza Zafar (11)	76
Zoe Nightingale (10)	78
Adam Faqir (8)	80
Aroosh Imaani Khan (10)	82
Zain Hafeez (10)	84
Romana Munnawwar Patel (9)	86
Isa Patel (9)	88
Ajwa Shah (9)	90
Inshal Munir Choudhary (9)	92

Umer Aayan Khaliq (8)	94
Sharik Ishtiaq (10)	96
Khadija Amer Choudrey (8)	98
Saniya Khan (9)	100
Rohan Gupta (7)	102
Zahra Ehsan (10)	104
Maryam Bhana (11)	106
Eshaal Imaani Khan (8)	108
Raees Khan Saghir (8)	110
Dua Fatima Rizvi (7)	112
Zaibaa Rahman (10)	113
Sahl Musa (8)	114
Karisma Jones (9)	115
Marwan Younes (7)	116
Ayaan Amanjy (8)	117
Adam Ehsan (9)	118
Darakhsha Munnawwar Patel (8)	119
Amira Wardingley (9)	120
Kiyham Mitchell (10)	121
Iqra Aslam (8)	122
Imaan Hussain (7)	123
Daniel Manuel (11)	124
Aisha Huda Mahmood (8)	125
Hasnain Babar (8)	126
Savio Santhosh (7)	127
Mohammed Yusuf Aslam (9)	128
Hira Zafar Iqbal (10)	129
Iman Lameche (8)	130
Anamta Shahzad (7)	131
Caitlyn McKay (10)	132
Daley Okiye (11)	133
Ayesha Raja (8)	134
Eimaan Noor Qadir (9)	135
Zainab Qadir (10)	136

St James' CE Primary School, Ashton-under-Lyne

Erin Jones (9)	137
Ahmad Lewis Abodunrin (9)	138
Preaw Barker (8)	140
Isabelle Fisher-Gould (8)	142
Oliwier Kurylo (9)	144

Klaudia Kleszcz (9)	146
Rimla Ahmed (9)	148
Gracie Pinto De Andrade (8)	150
Libby Johnson (8)	152
Jessica Herod (8)	153
Klea Ballabani (8)	154
Lennon Smith (9)	155
Mohammad Sahil (9)	156
Cody Edwards (8)	157
Abi-Jo Baker (8)	158
Ayaan Ashraf (8)	159
Marwah Jhangir (9)	160
Sana Hussain (8)	161

Unity Academy, Blackpool

Indy Simpson (8)	162
Alex Ozwu (8)	163
Paddy Jones (8)	164
Alexander Pittilla (8)	165
Milo Duffield (7)	166
Lynden Anderson (7)	167
Evie Sylvia Holmes (8)	168
Lucia Panayiotis (8)	169
Michael John Edwin Gill (8)	170
Courtney Bradley (8)	171
Emily Moore (7)	172

Westwood Prep School, Oldham

Dawud Mazafar (9)	173
Ismail Muhammad (8)	174
Muhammad Adam Rahim (8)	176
Adyan Hussain (9)	177
Rabeeah Noor (9)	178

The Diaries

The Incredible Diary Of... The Underpants Monkey!

Dear Diary,

Today was the most fun day of my life! I went to the park with my dad. I was on the swing, having fun while my dad was pushing me and then, all of a sudden, we both shouted, "Monkey!" The monkey was wearing white underpants with red hearts on them! In my head, I was a bit confused.

I jumped off the swing with excitement and shouted, "Come on Dad!" We both ran through the park and into the streets. We tried to catch up with the monkey. We kept on running and running until our legs felt like they were going to fall off. Trust me, he was a fast monkey!

Me and my dad chased him everywhere. I couldn't believe there was still a loose monkey on the run but it was getting dark, so we both walked home, panting heavily. As soon as we got home, I got dressed in my cosy PJs, then jumped into my warm bed.

Raisa Ahmed (9)

Bolton Parish Church CE Primary School, Bolton

The Incredible Diary Of... The Best Skateboard Ever

Dear Diary,

I was being sold at a market when a boy looked at my owner's shop. When he found out that I was being sold, he quickly asked my owner how much I was and he said £2.50. I was astonished because he'd bought me for £10! Then the boy ran to his mum and said that he wanted me! He asked his mum if she could buy me for him.

Then, out of nowhere, fingers grew on my shiny wheels. I crossed my fingers because, when people are nervous, they cross their fingers so that's what I did. The boy and his mum came and the boy's mum said that she wanted to buy me! My owner handed me over to them.

On the way to the boy's house, the boy introduced himself to me. Then I knew his name. His name was Tommy. When we arrived at Tommy's house, he quickly grabbed me and we went inside. He quickly put me down and he went to his room to get something. When he came back down, he brought a small house for me. Then I started feeling like I was at home!

The next day, Tommy asked his mum if he could go to the skate park. His mum said yes because it was Tommy's birthday. I hoped he wouldn't fall off me when we got there. He started to skate, he didn't know how to do tricks, so I did a backflip and jumped. Tommy was so happy that he couldn't even breathe! Then his mum came running and Tommy said he was okay.

Wasim Iftakhar (9)
Bolton Parish Church CE Primary School, Bolton

The Incredible Diary Of... The Crazy Werewolf

Dear Diary,

I saw some people walking in the park, then I growled. After that, I saw them going to another place in the ordinary old park. I decided to follow them. I then jumped from the bushes like a very wild lion, but they'd seen me coming and had started running quickly.

I started to get very tired. It all happened on a full moon night. I stopped, I couldn't see them anywhere. When I did, I howled. I was running as fast as I could but trying not to make a noise. Unfortunately, they saw me coming and started to run faster than they were running before!

Oh, I was tired, I was getting so tired! I couldn't even feel my legs! An idea came into my head and I grinned. I already knew what I had to do. It was an amazing idea, it would be a really good one. First, I would find out where they were, but I wouldn't chase them otherwise everything would be ruined.

Soon, I found out where they were. Then I went into the bushes and pounced on them. My heart was pumping with excitement. I jumped out from the bushes like a wild cat, but they saw me and started to run away. I didn't chase them, but I had another idea. I then saw them leave the park, making sure that the gates were locked...

Abbas Bin Usman (9)
Bolton Parish Church CE Primary School, Bolton

The Incredible Diary Of... The Spy Cat

Dear Diary,

I was an ordinary black cat at the pet shop until a huge, looming shadow bought me. It changed my cruel, lonely life forever because he was a spy! I couldn't believe my eyes. He had already set up my cat mansion!

Without further ado, I jumped on the luxury bed, saw the cat food and best of all... a laser! But I wasn't good enough for him because I was really lazy, so he dumped me! How could this happen to me?

I now knew how to be a spy because of my previous owner. I was called Spy Cat, I wore a black suit. Maybe this wasn't the end of me! It felt so cool to be back in the game. I left to get a taxi to the airport. Everyone needs to pay fares, so I paid. You won't believe who it was: my previous owner, Bob.

I ran out of the taxi, into the airport. Someone looked like a diamond smuggler. I followed him onto a plane going to Dubai. I could feel my blood rushing through my body and my legs were throbbing because I'd run so fast onto the plane.

It was a long journey. I followed him to his hotel room. He opened his suitcase... Diamonds! He saw me in the room. I thought it was the end of me, he was a robber! But he petted me! I guessed I now had a new owner...

Musa Baig (8)
Bolton Parish Church CE Primary School, Bolton

The Incredible Diary Of... My First Winter

Dear Diary,

I was just an ordinary tree in an ordinary forest. I was very happy, but something terrifying happened. All of my leaves began to fall off! The day after that, I saw white stuff all over the ground. My heart was beating at top speed when this happened. It was amazing!

Then, out of nowhere, my branches began to grow (it was probably because of the white stuff). How strange! My roots began to grow too! I was getting taller and taller every second.

A while later, I was the tallest tree on Earth! The only problem was that I had so many birds. I had heard one of my friends say that the white stuff was called snow. How good is that? I shrunk back to normal size and that was when I decided to invent the holiday called winter. Now, it happens every year!

Lilah Cameron (9)

Bolton Parish Church CE Primary School, Bolton

The Incredible Diary Of... The Fantastic Wimpy Kid

Inspired by 'Diary Of A Wimpy Kid' by Jeff Kinney

Dear Diary,

I saw this kid called Bob. He went to the football pitch, then he took a rotten egg out of his pocket. Then he cracked the egg and made a big smudge in the middle of the pitch. When I went to touch it, the bullies hit me in the eye and it turned black. The school called my mum and she took me to the opticians. They gave me some glasses and contact lenses. I went back to school and this kid called Stuart made a game up called Rotten Egg Touch. He had it for five months, then left. Then I had the Touch, people ran away from me, they were afraid! The principal shouted at me, then the bullies tried to hit me. They didn't because my big brother (called Jeff Jeffrison) is a boxer. He soon taught me how to punch them in their faces very hard!

Hashim Abbas (9)

Bolton Parish Church CE Primary School, Bolton

The Incredible Diary Of... A Ball Of Cotton

Dear Diary,

Don't even get me started on what happened yesterday. I don't want to talk about it... Fine, I'll tell you. I was in Asda on the shelf and a woman picked me up, bought me and took me home. I thought I was going to be made into a lovely, soft, woolly jumper like the other cotton balls, but no, I was wrong. I was given to an awful thing called a cat! Every moment, I got shorter and shorter. Now, I am quite short, but not quite at the end. The cat is always coming for me. I'm always out of breath. I get out of the rooms and lock the cat in there. The cat had another piece of me earlier and so I've nearly reached my death day today. As soon as the cat eats me, I will no longer exist...

Dior Destiny Boardman (9)
Bolton Parish Church CE Primary School, Bolton

The Incredible Diary Of... The Most Amazing Wizard

Dear Diary,

Today was the best day ever! I was accepted to Hogwarts by Professor McGonagall. Can you believe it? The head of Gryffindor! My mother and father are muggles by the way, so I'd not got much of a chance, that's why I'm lucky!

I went to Ollivander's and got my first wand, which hasn't broken yet. I met Professor Snape in Diagon Alley, I called him Professor Shape! There, I also became friends with Harry Potter's son, James Potter. I want to be in Gryffindor too! I literally want to do Charms straight away, but definitely not Potions because I will see Snape again! I wish my parents could come, but they can't because they haven't been accepted to Hogwarts.

Ahmad Shahid (8)
Bolton Parish Church CE Primary School, Bolton

The Incredible Diary Of...

Inspired by 'Diary Of A Wimpy Kid' by Jeff Kinney

Dear Diary,
Somebody ate the cheese and it was disgusting!
Then they had the Cheese Touch. I then got the
Cheese Touch because somebody passed it on to
me. I now need to pass it on to somebody else...

Lawson Parkinson (8)

Bolton Parish Church CE Primary School, Bolton

Cherry's Diary

Inspired by 'The Giant's Necklace' by Michael Morpurgo

Dear Diary,
I never thought I'd write a diary, but my mum wanted me to write one. I want to write today even though I'm a ghost. I want to tell you how I died. As another day turned, the day we were leaving our holiday, I was in the kitchen with my brothers. They were annoying me like every day. Today was a special day because I was going to finish the necklace.
In the cove, my mum and dad walked on the beach, my brothers were jumping in the rock pools and I was searching for the best pink shells. Then Mum and Dad and my brothers left me, but I didn't notice and kept digging.
On the beach, I was still looking for shells and did not notice a big wave which was rolling in. When the big wave hit, I did notice! When I noticed, it was too late. The sea had already covered the path home, so I had to scramble out of the cove. A big wave knocked me against the rocks. I felt dizzy and a wave covered my head...

Harris Brierley (11)
Gisburn Road Community Primary School, Barnoldswick

The Incredible Diary Of...

Inspired by 'The Giant's Necklace' by Michael Morpurgo

Dear Diary,

Today, I'm writing about how I died. Yes, I am a ghost. Cool right?

It all started in Zennor in Cornwall. We went for a family holiday and I was making a necklace. I was trying to reach the toaster by the next day, we had to leave then, and I was working so hard. I didn't want to stop. It shone beautifully and sparkled. Mum told me to take a long break because of how hard I was working, but I was too concentrated. As I swirled the cowrie shells, I heard a loud thump coming from upstairs.

As I carried on with self-belief, I heard my four brothers running downstairs. I weaved the shells onto the necklace, but then the four mistakes came and hovered over my fantastic artwork. They started to tease me, so I chased the pigs upstairs, screaming insults at them. The more I insulted them, the more they loved it. As I weaved the last shell, I realised I needed more cowrie shells, so off I went.

I dug for more cowrie shells, my brothers were in the rock pool area and Mum and Dad were sunbathing. As it was a hot day, my family went inside to cool down. It was only me and I carried on. I was gathering a lot of speed and my hope rose.

When I was digging for my last couple of shells, Boat Cove was forming a storm, but I was too distracted. I looked up to see that I only had a couple of seconds to get to safety, so I sprinted with my shells clutched to me! My sandy, wet hands gripped onto the worn-out rocks to get to safety. I knew I had a chance to finish collecting the cowrie shells, so I went back.

I had no time, I couldn't do it. I tried running back, but the tide hit my back and my eyes closed...

Brett Harper (11)
Gisburn Road Community Primary School, Barnoldswick

The Giant's Necklace

Inspired by 'The Giant's Necklace' by Michael Morpurgo

Dear Diary,

It's me again, I'm so annoyed because I never finished the necklace and I'm devastated that I... well, died. Being a ghost is so boring! My family and friends know that I am dead and they can't see me! I bet my brothers are having so much fun without me there bugging them 24/7. I miss being alive. Anyway, back to the necklace.

As usual, we all went down to the beach. My brothers played in the rock pools, my parents sunbathed and I looked for more cowrie shells, the pink ones to be precise. I knew I wasn't finished until the chain reached the toaster. Eventually, my family headed back home and I stayed at the cove, looking for the final fifty shells.

I was digging in the sand for what felt like hours and, every five or so minutes, I would find a shell. Boat Cove was calm and quiet at this point. I was all alone. If I wasn't so immersed in my search, I would have noticed the storm racing in. The waves were covering me at this point and I guess that's how I died, but I didn't know I had.

I tried to climb up the cliff a couple of times and then, I finally got to a tunnel in the ruined mine. In the mine, I found two friendly miners. We had a long and interesting conversation. After a while, they led me to the surface. I ran across the cliffside, along the fields and eventually made it home. The coast guard was sat at the table with my family, they were all in tears.

Anyway, I think you've heard enough. It makes me feel empty inside, probably because I am. I will write to you tomorrow...

Jamie Pearson (11)
Gisburn Road Community Primary School, Barnoldswick

The Giant's Necklace

Inspired by 'The Giant's Necklace' by Michael Morpurgo

Dear Diary,

I never normally write in my diary, so I thought I'd give it a shot since my mum has always wanted me to write in it. In real life, I'm actually not writing to you as I'm dead! Yes, you heard it right, I'm dead and I'm now a ghost! It's unreal. Let me tell you how it all began...

As usual, we were on holiday and it was another sweltering day. Unfortunately, it was our last few days there. As it was a beautiful morning, we decided to take a trip to the beach not far from where we were staying. Whilst my brothers played around in the rockpools, I started looking for some more cowrie shells as I was so close to reaching the toaster and only needed 150 more.

A few hours passed and Mum and Dad were packing away their sun loungers and towels, ready to head back. I still didn't have enough shells, so Mum and Dad said that I could stay behind a bit longer while they went to tidy the cottage. Mum and Dad gave me strict instructions: keep my hat on, don't bathe because I was alone and to be back well before dark. All of a sudden, a huge, grey cloud appeared above me - I wasn't aware of it.

Evening came, I began to shiver as the cold wind blew past my cheeks. I put on my sweater and jeans to keep me warm, that was when I saw the cloud. Not that I cared. I began digging once again since time was running out. That was when I realised that the tide was coming in and so, I began to search for rocks to clamber on... but I drowned.

Lia-J Lawson (10)

Gisburn Road Community Primary School, Barnoldswick

The Incredible Diary Of... Cherry And Her Necklace

Inspired by 'The Giant's Necklace' by Michael Morpurgo

Dear Diary,

This is the strangest thing that has happened to me... ever! Mum told me to write in my diary, but I didn't care. I was trying to finish off my necklace, my giant's necklace, and my brothers were harassing me, so I had to make them leave me alone. Mum told me to write, but I didn't listen. I wanted to reach the toaster and I needed 150 more shells.

Before we left the cottage, we went to Boat Cove, it was quiet. Mum and Dad got on sunbeds, my brothers went diving and I went off to find some pink cowrie shells.

A while passed and I had collected eighty shells, so I needed seventy more. That was when Mum, Dad and the boys left. Danger was coming. While I was doing my thing, the tide crashed onto the rocks, but I didn't notice. I needed the shells, so I dug as fast as I could. Then I noticed the tide!

I didn't know what to do, I only had a few shells left to get, so I dug and dug until I had enough shells. It was time to head back to the cottage. I started to climb the cliff to get home and the sea was rising. The tide was coming in like horses and I was petrified. I got to the edge when the sea dragged me down. I was no more...

Alfie Holman (10)
Gisburn Road Community Primary School, Barnoldswick

Cherry's Diary

An extract inspired by 'The Giant's Necklace' by Michael Morpurgo

Dear Diary,

I never thought I would write and keep a diary, but here I am. Anyway, I'm not really writing to you, I don't have superpowers! I'm no longer a normal girl like other girls in the world. I'm a ghost. Isn't that cool? But the reason I'm writing in you is to tell you how I became a ghost.

As usual, it was a boiling hot day and everything was just fine. It was the last couple of days of the holiday. I was determined to finish my giant's necklace, ignoring them. I had to reach the toaster as I'd told everyone I would. I only needed a few more pink cowrie shells and then it would be finished.

Later that day, we set off to Boat Cove. My brothers, who had lost interest in me, were already off rock-pooling. Mum and Dad were lounging in the sun, side by side on stripy deck chairs, enjoying the last few hours until we went home the next day. I set off, searching for my shells.

After a while, everyone got tired and went home to pack. I asked Mum if I could stay to collect more shells. She let me. I thought that hopefully, I had enough time to collect enough shells to complete the giant's necklace...

Lily Rogan (11)
Gisburn Road Community Primary School, Barnoldswick

The Diary Of The Ghost Of Cherry

Inspired by 'The Giant's Necklace' by Michael Morpurgo

Dear Diary,
How's it going? I never thought this would happen to me. I've never written a diary before 'cause I could never be bothered to, but just to let you know, I'm as dead as a dodo! I bet you want to know how I died.

As usual, it was a blazing hot day and the day was nice and normal. There were only a few days 'til I was going to go home. I needed to finish my giant's necklace. My four brothers, the four mistakes, were teasing me, but I ignored the lot of them. I wanted my necklace to reach the toaster. I only needed a few more shells.

We woke up in the morning and headed for the beach. I started to look for shells. It got really hot and my mum and dad went home. I knew I had enough time to go and collect more shells and I used it.

As I searched the sandy beach, I realised it was nearly sunset and I still needed more shells. I looked up and became aware that there was an angry-looking storm, but I only needed ten more shells, so I stayed.

All of a sudden, the furious tide was thrashing up at me and soaked my poor ankles. I didn't think I could survive! That was my last thought...

Mahek Noor Mahmood (10)
Gisburn Road Community Primary School, Barnoldswick

Cherry's Diary

Inspired by 'The Giant's Necklace' by Michael Morpurgo

Dear Diary,

I never normally do this, but it is important. I am not an ordinary girl anymore because I am dead - yes, you heard it right. I am devastated that my family can't see me anymore. I know that they are sat there, crying. I want you to know how I died...

We went to the beach and my brothers played on the rocks while my mum and I searched for cowrie shells, especially the pink ones. I searched for my cowrie shells until I realised that I only had a few hours left.

Then, all of a sudden, the raging clouds demolished the cheerful mist. A herd of white racehorses sprinted past. Minutes later, a reckless tide smashed over the shore. I needed fifty more shells, I thought it would only take ten minutes!

At this point, furious waves crashed against the cliff face. What was I going to do? The waves were getting closer to my toes, my belly felt like butterflies as I was dragged into the sea...

Isabelle Jesson (10)

Gisburn Road Community Primary School, Barnoldswick

The Incredible Diary Of... Daisy The Explorer

Dear Diary,

Today, I woke up at 6am and jumped out of bed, feeling nervous and excited. I went to the amazing Amazon Rainforest. I felt a little bit nervous because I thought I would be hurt by one of the animals. I went because I wanted to learn interesting information about the animals and plants that lived there.

Later on, I arrived in the amazing Amazon Rainforest. First, I saw cute, cuddly chimpanzees swinging across the tall, green trees. Next, I was amazed by the bright, colourful hummingbirds swooping gracefully across the bright blue sky. Then I saw dark blue butterflies flying elegantly above the amazing Amazon Rainforest.

After that, I went to look at the fascinating plants. First, I was shocked and surprised because I saw a huge Brazil nut tree. Then I was surprised by the bright, beautiful bromeliads blooming brightly. After an exhausting day, I sailed home across the crystal clear water in a small brown boat. When I was home, I slowly walked upstairs into my warm, cosy bed and fell fast asleep.

Daisy Walsh (9)

Lever House Primary School, Farington

The Incredible Diary Of... Jeff The Planet Pig

Dear Diary,

Yesterday was the weirdest day of my piggy life! It was just a normal day at the farm when, suddenly, a voice overhead greeted me. It was a holy space god named Faith! Pete the farmer, who was fast asleep in bed, didn't notice the strange noises going on outside. She seemed like a kind, lovely, old woman, but there was a small feeling inside my little piggy brain that maybe that wasn't true.

She kindly asked me if I wanted to visit her grand kingdom on an unknown planet named Spacetopia. At first, I wasn't sure, but then she offered me a lifetime supply of muddy puddles which I couldn't resist! Also, just in case, I took my trusty little piggy knife.

Off we went, swiftly soaring through the great Milky Way filled with bright, gleaming stars, like speeding cheetahs. Finally, we arrived in Spacetopia and all of Faith's loyal space robots stood guard in front of the kingdom. With many wondrous thoughts flying through my head, I slowly strolled along the crystal blue brick pathway into the kingdom.

More fully-suited robots greeted me, but then they started to surround me in a suspicious way. I couldn't believe it, they were turning against me! I knew there was something suspicious about them. Luckily, I still had my trusty piggy knife in hand, so I took a deep breath in, told my piggy heart I could do this and swiftly took them all out in one go! Thankfully, the evil god Faith surrendered and I was able to make it back home safely. As I was falling, a muddy puddle was in sight, so I aimed for that and *splat!* I belly-flopped straight into it. Even though I had to bravely take out those robots, it was still a good experience.

Joseph Rogers (9)
Lever House Primary School, Farington

The Incredible Diary Of... Ben Smith

Dear Diary,

Today was exciting and probably the happiest day of my life! I woke up at 5:39am, which is quite late for me! I struggled to get out of my comfy, warm bed, but I managed to. Suddenly, my phone started to ring loudly, it was my boss telling me to get up! I instantly agreed politely and started to get ready for the day. It took me a whopping three hours to get ready, a new Ben record! During the three hours, I got at least twelve phone calls from my boss. It was okay though because I have a time machine. I changed it back to nine o'clock and got to work on time.

My first food delivery was to a lovely old lady. She invited me for a cup of tea in her house because it was as cold as an iceberg outside. When I realised the time, I got very stressed in my head. I didn't know how to say 'I have to go now'. But when I did, she was understanding and gave me her number. My second delivery was to a kind, rich man but with a spoilt daughter, who I personally thought was a brat. I didn't say that though because it would be very rude. While I was going for lunch with my cool best mate, Stan, I got a surprise phone call from my boss!

Next thing I knew, I was in Buckingham Palace! I was delivering a feast to the Queen! She asked me what my dream was, I told her politely that I wanted to be a zookeeper for cute, cuddly elephants. She needed another zookeeper for her private zoo in the cute elephant section! I was overjoyed and so grateful.
I'm now in my big bedroom in the palace and I'm very happy!

Erin Cadence Gibbons (8)
Lever House Primary School, Farington

The Incredible Diary Of... Charlotte's Day

Dear Diary,

Today's been hectic and surreal. Let me tell you all about it. The day started with a late start, a late mark at school and a test I hadn't studied for. It wasn't a good start to the day.

After school, we had to go out for dinner which I wasn't happy about at first but, as we were walking towards the restaurant, guess who I saw? BLM Whalley! Only the best author ever! I've read all of her books! I had to get her autograph. Without telling anyone, I slipped away to follow her. Surprisingly, she led me into the zoo. I was so confused, why was she going in there? Well, that was soon to be answered.

Picking up my pace, I followed her into the red panda section. After following her this whole way, I had a nervous breakdown. I couldn't talk to her, could I? I decided to stay where I was for a bit. After a minute or two, she saw me and told me not to tell anyone what she was doing. Then I came to the realisation that she was stealing a red panda! I asked her to stop, but she didn't reply. A few seconds later, though it felt like hours, she was gone. After that, some park rangers caught me. I tried to tell them about what had happened, but they didn't listen. I tried to tell my parents when I was returned to them, but they didn't listen. Now, stuck in my room, I can't help wondering if I could've done anything to save the day. I'll report back tomorrow.

Isabel Pearson (10)
Lever House Primary School, Farington

Dreams Can Come True

Dear Diary,

It is Charlie-Rose writing if you didn't know. Today was the most phenomenal day ever, so I decided to write about it. Today started off like any other day: I ate my Coco Pops and got ready for school. But then, as I got ready to go out, Mum shouted from upstairs. She said that she had just remembered that today was the day I was supposed to go on the school trip to the marine animal rescue centre. I was ecstatic! I had always loved sea creatures, but the closest I had ever got to one was the tuna at the fishmonger. Now I would actually get to see some!

I ran to school as fast as I could. As I turned the corner to go into school, there it was, the huge coach that would be taking us to the centre. Half an hour later, we were there. Surprisingly, it was quite a shabby place with moss all over the walls, but I didn't care. All I cared about was getting to the dolphins as quickly as possible!

I raced up the stairs to the dolphin tank. When I got up there, I saw them, the most beautiful creatures I had ever seen. They were leaping in the air, their silver-skinned backs glistening. Their tails flicked in the air as they dived into the water and I could not resist, I had to jump in with them!

As I dived into the satin blue water, it was thrilling. I felt like one of the dolphins! As I swam through the water, something brushed my cheek and I realised I was swimming with the dolphins!

Isabella Blackburn (10)

Lever House Primary School, Farington

The Incredible Diary Of... India Spark

An extract

Dear Diary,
Like every other day, I woke up. A fairly normal day, nothing to worry about. Or, at least, I didn't think there was. My mum called me down for breakfast. As I was going downstairs, something caught my eye. The nearby volcano of Red Mountain was smoking. I thought nothing of it of course, but there was a part of me that thought it was related to the recent tremors.
Sitting down at the table, I began to eat my porridge, listening to the endless crashing of the waves on the shore. The rest of my family were unusually silent, not counting my dad due to the fact that he is almost always engrossed in a crossword. I hadn't realised what time it was until my mum's voice broke the silence. She was telling me to hurry up. With that, I got my bag and set off for school.
My teacher, who was talking about the large chance that Red Mountain would erupt despite the fact that the news would have put a warning in place, gave out some plans for a boat and told us to get into groups of eight. I think everyone was as

confused as I was. Once we had sorted ourselves out, Mr Bacroft explained what we were doing. I slowly walked towards the supply table and picked up everything we'd need. Every second seemed to drag on for what seemed like a day. After what felt like a month, our group had finished. Just in time too...

Emily Joan Mamwell-Holme (9)

Lever House Primary School, Farington

Black And White

An extract

Dear Diary,
Today started like any other day, the sun rose over the warm sea and the moon went down below the hills. Yawning, I rolled over to my bedside table. It was like this most mornings. Since my mum and I first came to live with Grandma in Southport, I had felt free from the outside world. I made friends too. Agatha (my grandma's next-door neighbour's daughter) had come round with cookies made from homemade batter. We sat down by the pier for hours, just talking. Ever since then, she would bring cakes, brownies or shortbread. Once, she even made black and white cakes because she had said they reminded her of us. I always dressed up in pink with my hair full of glitter, but Aggie (my nickname for her) would always wear black.
It was me and her against the world, just Aggie and Maisy. That is why I was so scared today. At twelve o'clock, Aggie came to the door with a basket full of muffins. I remember the way we laughed as we ran to the beach, her high-pitched cackle against my light giggle.

After a while of splashing each other in the water, we lay back down on our towels to dry off. I picked up my copy of Wonder and began to flick through the pages. This was what happened when one of us was reading and the other was bored - the bored one found fun. Agatha ran down the beach twice, then didn't come back...

Octavia Mae Nicholson-Blezard (10)
Lever House Primary School, Farington

The Incredible Diary Of...
Crystal The Sparkly Unicorn

Dear Diary,

You will not believe what happened today! First of all, I went round to Paige the pretty Pegasus' house. Although it was sunny, we decided to stay inside and decorate our skirts with sequins that shimmered. When we had finished, I decided to use my magic to make the sequins flip up and down, rainbow to silver. We had a fashion show. Meanwhile, my friend Luna and her little sister Midnight were galloping around. Luna was raising the moon and Midnight was raising the stars. Paige, me, Alice the amazing alicorn and Paloma the perfect pony decided to have a fly until morning.

Alice used her magic to make me and Paloma fly and we were off! We watched Luna and Midnight raise the moon and stars. As we were flying, something terrible happened. We were soaring through the sky when Alice's magic stopped! Midnight saw this and quickly used one of her stars to catch me and Paloma.

Once we were safely on the star, the others tried to help us up. They couldn't. We had to sleep on the star until morning. When the stars lowered, we seized our chance and leapt off. We ran home and found Alice and Paige on the way.

When we got home, we had pizza and sweets. I went to bed and found four necklaces. One was pink, one was purple, one was dark blue and one was light blue. We put them on and felt tingly.

Imogen Winters (8)
Lever House Primary School, Farington

The Incredible Diary Of... Socks The Cat

Dear Diary,

I am writing to tell you about how my day went. For my breakfast, I had a huge, chunky and juicy fish. I absolutely loved it! Then I had a little cat nap. I woke up and started running all over the place. I went in and out of the table legs, all around the settee and I even jumped on the beds! Then it was dinner time. It was chicken and fish cat food. Although it was a weird mix, it was still delicious. After dinner, I happily played with my favourite squeaky mouse toy. It made me feel warm inside. Near the settee is my bed, it is so soft and padded. I love my house!

Then I took a long slurp of water. I quickly ran behind the chair because I'd heard a loud bang. It was my scratching post, it had fallen over. While I was hidden behind the chair, my owner was looking for me. She finally found me. She gently whispered to say that everything was fine, then she left.

I felt so lonely without her. I played with my feathers for a bit and ran around a lot. The sun was shining brightly, I could hardly see! Suddenly, the clouds covered up the sun. I was petrified! It started hailing. Since it was hailing, I decided to take another nap.

When I woke up, the sun was shining again. I felt so relieved, I jumped on the settee and started jumping about. Finally, I had my juicy, fishy cat food for tea.

Sofia Alexa Higgins (7)

Lever House Primary School, Farington

The Incredible Diary Of... Hovis The Guide Dog

Dear Diary,

Today has been amazing! I was led into the garden, chewing on my bone, while my owner was still asleep. I saw a ginger tomcat trot past and, well, I tried not to bark. I let out a little yap, but luckily I didn't wake her up. I wanted to chase it so badly! Then I spotted a rabbit and chased that. I missed it this time. Then I spotted a bird that a cat had killed and it had lots of bones. I couldn't resist but to go and chew on the bones.

I jumped over the white wooden fence and grabbed the bones. But then, the ginger tomcat returned. I started to chase after it for miles and, when I finally caught up with the cat, it climbed up a large, tall tree. That was when I realised that I didn't know my way back home! I started to sniff around for my owner's scent, but I couldn't pick it up. I knew my owner would be worried.

I was what my owner called 'lost'. My owner needed me to guide her way! That's what I've been training for ever since I was a puppy. She's not blind, and she's not deaf, but she really struggles to get around. I knew I had to find my way home somehow. I went to sleep as it was getting dark.

I woke up in a bed with my owner cuddling up in the blankets at the end of the bed. Was I found? Did I walk home? Was it all a dream?

Hannah Grace Dobson (9)

Lever House Primary School, Farington

Sam's Incredible Diary

An extract

Dear Diary,

What a day! It started off with a basic morning, well, as basic as it can on a day like this. Waking up with endless ticks of the clock running through my ears, I opened my eyes as a rush of excitement ran through my body; it was my birthday! You have no idea how excited I was!

Turning towards the face of the clock, which was visible in the rising sun, I saw the time: 3:17am. I knew it would take me years to go back to sleep, but I still curled up with my eyes shut tightly in the hope that my mum would come to wake me up soon.

Hearing my mum's soft voice calling my name inside my head, I impatiently waited for something to happen. As each second dragged on, I heard nothing but birds tweeting. Can you imagine how frustrated I was? Bored, I stepped towards my mahogany bedroom door. I wanted an adventure and I wanted it now!

I jogged until I had an unbearable thirst. Resting on the pavement, I blinked again and again. I couldn't believe my eyes; the hopelessly boring world around me had turned into a beach! Could you cope with this shock? Looking around, I saw that the beach was miles long, but I was the only one on it. The beach had everything, even rides! You could only imagine a place like that!

May Hardy (10)
Lever House Primary School, Farington

The Incredible Diary Of... Wolf

An extract

Dear Diary,

Today was the weirdest day ever! It all started at 7am when Charlie, my older brother, woke me up with a bike horn. I was furious! He told me that I had to get ready for a hike in the forest as he and Jacob (my younger brother) had to get a scout badge or something like that.

Luckily, it was only a two mile drive to the nearby forest, so at least I didn't have to wait long. By the time we got there, I realised there was no phone service for my online map! Unfortunately, me and Jacob had no choice but to rely on Charlie's terrible map reading skills.

As we strolled through the forest, I heard a slight panting noise, like a wolf. This startled me so much that I lost focus on where I was going and stumbled back into Charlie, who lost his grip on the map and dropped it in the pond. He was as angry as a baby who'd had their dummy taken off them. I mean, come on, it's only a map!

Suddenly, we realised Jacob had wandered off. At this point, I was starting to panic! Then, you won't believe this, but Jacob flew past me and Charlie. Jacob wasn't alone, he was on a wolf! No joke! Suddenly, more wolves came, two stopping right next to us. Without thinking, we leapt on. It was amazing!

Abigail Doran (10)
Lever House Primary School, Farington

Christmas Away From Home

Dear Diary,

These past couple of days have been hectic! It was Christmas Eve and I was feeling excited. Then disaster struck! I wandered into the kitchen to ask my mum when we were going to put up the Christmas tree. I saw everyone packing! Scared, I asked Mum what was going on and she asked me to get in the car. Panicking, I walked over to Dad and he said not to worry because Mum had already packed for me.

I started to get really confused when Mum started to herd me, my big sister (Lauren) and my little sister (Kacy) into the car. After we had been driving for a while, I saw a sign that said, *Airport*. Everything started to make sense to me. We were going on holiday!

Once we had boarded the plane, I felt really excited, especially as I had a whole row of seats to myself. After the captain had announced that the seatbelt sign would turn off, I jumped out of my seat and asked Mum where we were going. She said it was a surprise. I felt even more excited!

Once we had got off the plane, we jumped into our hire car. I then realised that Kacy had been screaming and that my mum had been singing old-

50

fashioned songs! It was then that I knew it was going to be a long holiday...

Maisy Thornley (10)

Lever House Primary School, Farington

The Diary Of Hammy The Hamster

Dear Diary,

I can't wait to tell you what happened today! I went to a planet called Planet Demonster and met a demon hamster. He was a large, scaly demon with ferocious red horns on his head. I was scared out of my skin! Unfortunately, I was knocked out. When I had recovered, I called my cousins to come to the planet. I was still a bit dizzy when I woke up, but my cousins were on their way. The red-hot horns had gone. My cousins carefully took me to the vet's, even though they had wet tails.

After I had been checked on, my cousins went in and after that, we all felt a bit poorly. Then we realised that the vets were demons too! We thought it was the end for us, but before we died, we went on a mission to find all the demons on Planet Demonster.

First, we saw a policeman, then we found a surgeon, then a teacher, a dinner lady and then an office lady. Once we had found every demon, we went to England with their tools. The demons popped when we defeated them!

Everybody ate chocolate fudge cake to celebrate our victory. The other hamsters thought there was no wacky world. We all went to the wacky world, eating pizza and garlic bread!

Isaac Travers (8)
Lever House Primary School, Farington

The Incredible Diary Of... Dave

Dear Diary,

What an amazing day! I have had a really scary but interesting journey. I went back to the Stone Age! I was in my basement, creating a time machine to find more parts in the future for a machine: the clothes machine. The switch on the time machine was stuck and it was pointing to 20,000 years ago!

I was in my basement, making a time machine, as you already know. I went into it to fix the switch, but I knocked into the 'take off' button. Before I knew it, I was travelling through space-time! When I slowly landed, Stone Age people were trying to make a fire, good thing I'd brought a camera with me. I took some pictures, but suddenly the Stone Age people started to chase me! I had no idea why they were chasing me, probably because I didn't look like them.

Like the rapids, I raced quickly to the time machine with stones being thrown behind me. I quickly jumped into the time machine and raced through space-time. Luckily, I managed to get back. I tried to show people my pictures, but no one believed me. I'll tell you about other adventures soon, if I have any more.

Joshua Privett (9)
Lever House Primary School, Farington

The Incredible Diary Of...
Hermione Underwater

Dear Diary,

I was on the Hogwarts Express, finding my seat next to Harry and Ron. Eventually, I found them eating chocolate and sweets. There was a whole trollyfull of sweets scattered all over the table! "Save some sweets for me!" I laughed.

As soon as I put the second sweet in my mouth, we felt the train lurch sideways. "What's happening to the train?" Harry and Ron said together. They both laughed, "Jinx!"

Just then, a lady came in. She said that the train had fallen over the side of a bridge! Suddenly, mine, Harry and Ron's window flew open and we were thrown outside! We plummetted to our deaths. I had my eyes tightly shut so I had no idea what picked us up.

I dared to open my eyes to see that I could breathe underwater! The even crazier part was that a dolphin asked us if we were okay! We all said yes. The dolphin said that he would jump up, put us on the train and lift the train back onto the track. We all cheered.

The dolphin did as he said, we got back on the train and went to Hogwarts. I hope tomorrow is just as exciting as today!

Grace Langley (7)
Lever House Primary School, Farington

The Diary Of Paul Pogba And Marcus Rashford!

Dear Diary,

I'm Marcus Rashford and I have a brother called Paul Pogba. I was sprinting down the pitch when Paul Pogba passed to me. When I was running for the ball, someone behind me was catching up. As soon as I looked behind me, I saw that it was Lionel Messi! Before he caught up, I passed to my brother.

My brother got tackled horribly. Barcelona, who had the loudest crowd, got the ball and ran for the goal. In front of the player was Fred. Fred quickly went for the ball and was behind the player. Fred slid and tackled. He got a frustrating yellow card. He was in trouble!

Because he had a yellow card, he couldn't tackle anyone on the wet, slippery grass. This was turning into a rubbish day for him.

The next bright and sunny day, me and my brother went to lovely-smelling McDonald's. Although it was mine and my brother's favourite, it still took nearly four hours to get the food. Eventually, we ordered lovely, beautiful chips, massive chicken burgers and some tasty ketchup. It was yummy!

As soon as we had eaten it all, we went home before it was dark.

Harry Thomas French (8)
Lever House Primary School, Farington

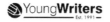

SpongeBob's Unbelievable Adventure!

Dear Diary,

Today, I woke up in the morning, feeling great as always. Leaping out of bed, I put on my square suit and stampeded out of my pineapple house, which always makes me hungry. Smiling, I walked down the street when a cannon rolled out of an alleyway. Abruptly, I got stuffed into the cannon and fired out of the ocean and onto land! Shaking, I scanned my surroundings; it was then that I realised I was on a volcano (Krakatoa)! I could see an emerging figure slowly walking towards me. Recoiling, I looked up at them. "Go away," I mumbled.

As my vision got better, I could tell that it was SpongeJoe SquarePants! When I was younger, Joe and I used to play on the shore until, one day, someone grabbed him and took him away. Suddenly, the volcano started to shake and rumble; lava started oozing out of the volcano. *Whoosh!* Ash, gas and rocks burst upwards from the lid and powered down towards us! Sprinting, Joe and I ran for our lives down the volcano, the pyroclastic flow struck from behind and launched us back into the ocean! What a day!

Nicholas Christopher Morley (10)
Lever House Primary School, Farington

The Incredible Diary Of... The Doggy Knight

Dear Diary,

Today, I've been sleeping to get my energy. I'm training to be a doggy knight. I'm a dog and I am very brave. I live in a castle. My trainer, George, has given me my strong, metal armour and today I started to attack a pretend enemy. I stopped because I got tired of the hard work.

Dear Diary,

Today, I woke up because of a very loud noise. It was George with a metal pipe. What was he doing? I opened my door and he was just getting me to wake up! I walked back into my room and waited while George set up the training room. Finally, George was ready. I got up and walked over to the training room. I attacked the pretend enemy-like soldier.

Dear Diary,

I was asleep in bed this morning, but then a bird knocked with its beak on my window. I got up, I was excited and joyful because it was my very last training day! I was also a bit scared and worried because I thought I might not pass. I set off to the training room. I did my best with everything. I got my results, I was so happy it was a pass!

Harry Walker (9)

Lever House Primary School, Farington

The Diary Of Ronaldo

Dear Diary,

I can't wait to tell you what happened today! I'm Ronaldo, you won't believe what happened today! I was walking to my coach and I was five minutes late. The driver said I had to give him £10, so I got in and set off, but my manager rang me and said, "If you don't get here in twenty, you will be dropped for ten games."

I hung up the phone. I was shaking, so I told the driver to hurry up. Since my manager called me, I was rattling. It didn't get better. I was stuck in a traffic jam because there were roadworks going on! When the driver stopped, a motorbike came speeding past. While my arm was out the window, the motorbike caught me on my hand. There were no bandages in the coach.

We got to the airport because my training ground is in Spain. While I was waiting for the plane, I went to a food shop called Subway. It was the only shop there, but I realised that it was closed. My flight was delayed too, but then I realised it wasn't my flight...

Thomas Harry Masterson (8)

Lever House Primary School, Farington

Underwater Experience

Dear Diary,

Today, I woke up to the thought of going into the deepest part of the ocean. Excitement rising, I set off towards the beach to my personal submarine. A few minutes later, my submarine came into sight as I turned the corner. Nearly screaming with excitement, I hopped in, checked that all of my gears worked, strapped myself in and sank into the underwater world.

After what seemed like forever, my submarine landed with a thud in the deepest part of the sea. You will never guess what I saw down there. I noticed a fish that seemed to have a transparent head; it seemed to have jelly inside. Surprised at this strange fish, my submarine slowly floated up. I suddenly jerked back the lever that stopped the submarine.

There was a fish near a crab, hypnotising it by changing its colours and then, *snap!* The fish had eaten the crab whole! Floating up to the surface, I felt amazed at the hypnotising fish. The head of the submarine popped up above the water and I saw land.

Megan Mahoney (10)
Lever House Primary School, Farington

The Incredible Diary Of... The Simpsons In Space

Dear Diary,

Today, I woke up and got dressed, then went downstairs to get some breakfast. On the way down, I saw Homer reading a newspaper for the first time in my life. He asked me if I wanted to have a tour of NASA. At first I didn't want to go, but then I heard there was an entertainment area with laser tag, I was in! I couldn't wait to go there. Eventually, we got there. Our first stop was the laser tag. I played a few rounds. I won two, drew one and lost one before we went to lunch. After lunch, we went on a tour of Apollo 11. As soon as Homer got there, he was dancing around in happiness.

When he got inside, Homer touched everything he saw. In the rocket was me, Homer and other visitors looking at the control part where all the buttons were and the seats. Curiously, I saw Homer looking at something, so I came over and saw his hand over the 'blast off' button. He pressed it and we went to space!

Thomas Sheehan (8)

Lever House Primary School, Farington

The Incredible Diary Of... Splat's Life

Dear Diary,

Today, I travelled to the ship where the next contest was being held. I got there and saw the cup. I'd tried so much for that cup. I saw the best squid in the contest. It was King. I won the first game using my worst gun. After that, I nearly lost my last game because they spotted me before I had the chance to change back into a human! I managed to get through. There were four winners but only two could go through. I got in and King did too.

As I was starving, I grabbed something to eat. When I was done, I went to the ship. As I was walking down to the ship, someone pushed me into the ocean. I saw another squid and a shark, they started chasing me! I found a ship to get on. I thought I was safe before I realised it was the piranhas' training ship! I was chased to the end of the ship and I jumped off and got back to write this.

Lucas Whish (8)

Lever House Primary School, Farington

The Incredible Diary Of... Grace

Dear Diary,

Today was a terrible day! A group of people were being really mean, all because I am disabled! I thought it would be a nice, relaxing day at the fun park, but it wasn't. It happened on a nice, sunny day.

Firstly, I finished my breakfast, which was delicious. Then I got my shoes on and went to get my busy family. We were halfway to the fun park when I saw a group of people that were tall and wore black boots. I started to play on the blue swings while my family was on the yellow slide.

After I had played on the swings, I felt so tired. Then a group of people came up to me, the ones I'd seen earlier. They said that I didn't belong there! I was so upset and heartbroken. I went into my pink and purple bed and put my head on my white pillow.

Madeline Briers (9)

Lever House Primary School, Farington

The Incredible Diary Of... SpongeBob

Dear Diary,

I live in a pineapple house with my seasnail. The booming sound of my clock rang through my head. I leapt out of bed and did my business.

I strolled into the Krusty Krab restaurant, but a terrible sight met my eyes. Plankton had frozen the Krusty Krab and mind-controlled everyone! Patrick had just arrived at the chaos. Both of us were so fearful, we dashed into the toilet. The toilet was full of bubbles, so we had a bubble party and went crazy.

Then we came out and gave in but, as quick as a flash, I turned into a wizard with a guitar, freed the people, stomped on Plankton and saved the Krusty Krab. The day was saved! I became one of the bosses at the Krusty Krab and I have to say, it was the best day of my life!

Ehren Munday (8)
Lever House Primary School, Farington

The Incredible Diary Of... The Lorax

Dear Diary,

One tired morning, I (the Lorax) stomped into the supermarket and all the other creatures stared at me like I was their prey. As soon as I placed my gigantic hand into a potato box, I unexpectedly disappeared into thin air! Then I realised that I had teleported to a world of rides! It was the adventure park!

Firstly, when I came back from the rides, my belly started to rumble. I decided to order the whole McDonald's menu because I was so hungry. Then I became fat and my belly popped open. I went to bed and I woke up on a roller coaster!

Finally, I grabbed the magic potato and it set me off to where I belong. When I was in the park, I got dizzy and I magically went home.

Aaron Holland (8)

Lever House Primary School, Farington

The Incredible Diary Of...
Hermione Granger's Adventure

Dear Diary,

Harry has been gone for a few days, this is getting suspicious. I have started my journey to find him, but I have realised that I'm not prepared. Although I have magic, I have no weapons, I am weak. I'm in the enchanted wood. I have fought evil mythical creatures. I have also become friends with nice mythical creatures that have guided me through the enchanted woods.

I hope that Harry is okay. I wish that Harry could just teleport to me. I have set up a camp and my mythical friends protect me. Every hour, it is getting hotter as the sun rises. I hunt for berries and I drink water from the streams. I *will* find Harry...

Paige Hardiman (8)

Lever House Primary School, Farington

71

Squish And The Flying Cow!

Dear Diary,
Today was absolutely life-changing and I mean it!
I'm not exactly sure if it was a dream though.
Anyway, I was bullied a lot, I never fit in with
anyone. I was making my way to school, all alone
as usual but when I was almost there, something
strange caught my eye. It glistened and shone. As I
got closer and closer, it got bigger and bigger. The
second I got there, it turned into a sparkly portal! I
was dying to get in, so I did. I finally opened my
eyes and there I was, in another dimension! I was
amazed. There was a flying cow! I took it home
and became famous at school.

Sofia Elizabeth Morley (8)

Lever House Primary School, Farington

The Incredible Diary Of...

Dear Diary,

I am writing to you to tell you that I had the most exciting day ever! While I was sleeping in my bed, I heard a little noise. Quickly, I jumped out of bed to check where it was coming from. Quietly, I tiptoed to the kitchen and crept up to the table and my toy Minion, Bob, was lying next to a bowl of bananas.

I thought that my brother must have been playing with it and put it there. I left the kitchen. Suddenly, I heard a loud bang. I went back to the kitchen and saw that Bob had come to life and the bowl of bananas had tipped out onto the Minion's head!

I took the Minion and looked in its eyes and went back to sleep. Suddenly, I heard a shooting noise. When I opened my eyes, I saw the Minion using a laser from his eyes! I tried everything to stop him, but it didn't work.

Soon, I went to bed and woke up and a whole army was on my bed! I called my brother and asked how to turn them back to normal. He said, "Give them bananas."

I gave all the Minions some bananas and they all turned back to normal.

Eham Zaman (10)
Queen Elizabeth's Grammar School, Blackburn

The Incredible Diary Of... Joey

13th October 2017

Dear Diary,

In the evening, I was trying to write a book. It was a diary and, as soon as I wrote the date, a portal appeared. Things got weird! A person came out of the portal and said, "Hello, my name is Joey Junior, nice to meet you. What's your name?"

I said, "Joey. I'm writing a book, can you help me?"

He answered, "Yes, what's it about?"

"I don't know."

"Then how are you going to write it?"

"I don't know!" Then the confusion ended and it was time for bed.

14th October 2017

Dear Diary,

Today was an interesting day, we went to the forest and fought a jaguar! We looked closely at a poison dart frog too. We made an invention that can send you anywhere, anytime. We used it to teleport to a fortress back in time and we saw King Henry V. We defeated his army with a machine gun, rocket launcher and grenades!

The day is finally over, it is 2:35am!

16th October 2017
Dear Diary,
Oh my goodness, I slept for a day! I needed to get my book, it wasn't even finished. Double J was already awake and scribbling in my book! I went up to him and he had finished it. I didn't need to worry, all I needed to do was give it in.
After we gave it in, we wanted to go on YourAncestor.com and something strange was there. When Joey Junior searched 'Who is my great, great grandfather', it was me! Joey!
"How is this possible?"
"I don't know!"
"Wait, do you know the stories? You only have a certain amount of time to send people back! Come on, we need to send you back!"
"Okay bye."
All I had to do was write which year he was from: 3036. He went through the portal. "Bye forever!"

Umar Karolia (9)
Queen Elizabeth's Grammar School, Blackburn

My Adventures With Jeff

Dear Diary,

I have to tell you about what happened today. This morning, Dad gave me a puppy whose name is Jeff. He is so cute and fluffy with a white body and blue eyes. He is the cutest puppy in the world and not just that, when I had him in my hand, I went into my room and the dog went all bright. Then in a second, I was somewhere I didn't know!

When it wasn't foggy anymore, I looked around to have a look at people. Jeff was still with me, he took my sleeves in his mouth and took me to a man, an old man, who didn't have very warm clothes on on such a cold, windy day. He looked very hungry.

When I looked at him, I put my hand inside my pockets and took out all the money which my dad gave to me as a bonus. I softly put the money in the man's hand and then looked at my empty pockets, but I was so proud that I had helped someone!

After all that, I turned around and found myself in another place. I looked around again, but I saw something, something like paper, but shinier than that. I bent down and saw that it wasn't a piece of paper, it was money! Double the money I gave to the old man! But I thought there would be someone else who needed help because, before I'd moved, a man needed my help. Who needed help now?

It was a woman who'd lost her twin girls. I looked at Jeff and he smelt the hats of the twins. He was finding them like a police dog and, at last, he found them. After that, I was home and hoping I had more people to help with Jeff.

Fizza Zafar (11)
Queen Elizabeth's Grammar School, Blackburn

The Life Of James Adams

Inspired by 'CHERUB' by Robert Muchamore

Dear Diary,

I've just got off my first mission, it was exhausting. I was terrified that I'd mess it up and the mission would be terrible. That didn't happen, I am so relieved! The worst part was that I had to leave my first girlfriend and I loved her quite a lot, so I miss her so very much. As you already know, she's called Joanna and we basically did everything together. I'm just very pleased the mission went well and helped. Earth was kind of taken down. We pretty much knew where people had gone, but the rest was for the intelligence's that involve adults, not children.

I'm glad we're out of that dump, Fort Harmony. I had to sleep in the same room as Agent Amy Collins and even had to sleep on the floor! My sister, Lauren, will do her basic training soon. I'm so proud of her, she's going to be an agent just like me. I still can't believe CHERUB exists and I'm an actual agent too!

Ever since I arrived at CHERUB, everything has been pretty much perfect. To be able to become an agent, you have to be very good at something, like a subject (not including sports). I was amazing at maths, but nothing else really. So, that's how I

got into CHERUB.
CHERUB has been the biggest thing I've ever done and I enjoyed my first mission. I cannot wait until my next mission. I'm tired and should get to bed now. That's that for today. I'll probably write in this diary tomorrow...

Zoe Nightingale (10)
Queen Elizabeth's Grammar School, Blackburn

The Incredible Diary Of... Bouncy Bob

Dear Diary,

My day started with me jumping out of bed. As soon as my feet touched the floor, my legs started to bounce. I bounced from morning to night. I couldn't help bouncing everywhere. Bouncing made me happy, but it drove everyone crazy. "Please, please stop bouncing for a second!" is all I heard.

I thought, *if only I could live on an island with people like me, my life would be a dream.* Whilst listening to a story being told, I dreamt away. I dreamt I was going on an adventure. I found an B-shaped island. I was excited to see this island, so I climbed out of the boat, trying to move quietly. My legs gave in and started bouncing. *Oh no!* I thought. I was feeling scared. Out of nowhere, I heard a quiet, gentle voice saying, "Hello, I'm Lucy. Who are you?"

Startled, I murmured, "Bouncy Bob..."

"Welcome to our island of bounce. Come, let's meet the rest!"

The rest? I thought quietly to myself. I followed Lucy, she was bouncing around. I was surprised, overwhelmed with excitement! Without realising it,

I started bouncing. I heard people clapping. "You have some good skills!" a boy shouted. "Do it again!"
I started bouncing slowly as everyone started encouraging me. I was feeling happy. Off I went, showing off my skills. Everyone joined in bouncing around. No one yelled at me to stop, I felt like I was in heaven!

Adam Faqir (8)
Queen Elizabeth's Grammar School, Blackburn

The Incredible Diary Of... Our Trip To Blackpool Water Park

Dear Diary,

Today, we went to Blackpool Water Park. Once we got there, we got changed and jumped into the pool and warmed our bodies up. We all had so much fun playing on the slides and splashing around with everyone. The slides were so big and fast, I could not believe it! It was like I was on a really fast ride just outside of the water park.

Me and my brother decided to go on the fastest, coolest and scariest slide in the whole of the UK! Off we went to the biggest queue I have ever seen. While we waited for ages and ages, all the others decided to take my sister to a smaller slide while we weren't there to entertain her.

Finally, we went down the amazing, zooming slide. It was so fast that I could hear my brother scream like a little girl! It was so fun, until we came to the bottom and realised my family had gone! We looked for them, but we couldn't find them. I thought it would be a good idea if we split up. We both looked, but it didn't work!

I had no one with me and I was so scared. This fear was scarier than when I was on the slide earlier. I looked and looked, but I could not see them anywhere! Then I thought of the likeliest place and I got an idea. They could be at the baby slide! I went there and guess who I found? Everyone waiting for me, including my brother!

After that, we went to Nando's and then we went home and went to bed. I will write to you soon.

Aroosh Imaani Khan (10)

Queen Elizabeth's Grammar School, Blackburn

The Incredible Diary Of...

Dear Diary,

Today, the best and the worst thing ever happened to me. In the morning, I was thinking of a way to complete my formula accurately for my invincibility serum when I suddenly came up with an idea! I rushed to the lab as fast as lightning. I put my brilliant idea into action and then, before I knew it, my idea had worked! It turned a silver colour like I'd predicted and smelt like peppermint as I'd also predicted. All that was left was to test it.

I injected myself with it and punched myself with a robotic arm I'd invented. The arm snapped and the hand broke without me feeling the slightest contact. I jumped up, laughing in happiness! I hid it away in a special box inside a reinforced titanium alloy, safe with a biometric palm scanner and a facial and iris identification scanner back up lock with a reinforced electronic tumbler.

It was getting late, so I decided to get some sleep. Suddenly, during the night, a loud and powerful explosion occurred in my house. When the police, fire engines, MI7, MI5, MI6 and the SAS arrived, I unfortunately discovered that my laboratory (including all my research) had been destroyed and annihilated purposely!

Not long after, I was informed that they had confirmed it was terrorists and that they were sweeping the entire area for DNA or fingerprints or any other evidence that could help them find the people who had caused so much damage.

Zain Hafeez (10)

Queen Elizabeth's Grammar School, Blackburn

Diary Of A Wimpy Kid

Dear Diary,

Today, I went to camp and, at night, we played a game called Tie The Rope. First, we tied the rope to our hands and we had to use teamwork to get the water bucket from the other side of the cabin and we had to put the bucket in the cabin. We had no water left in ours! Every time we went, we lost the game because we apparently didn't use enough teamwork.

Dear Diary,

Today, we were told that we were working on a farm like in the olden days. Despite all of that, my dad wrote a letter to me. It went like this, 'How are you doing in camp? Are you failing in everything or are you passing everything? If you are failing, don't fail any more things.'
In the night, we roasted marshmallows and had a campfire and we made our beds to sleep. Once we got to sleep, I felt a tickle on my arm. I rolled my sleeves up and, whilst that happened, we heard spooky sounds! We all huddled up and we stayed up until midnight and then we fell asleep.

Dear Diary,

This morning, we woke up and our teacher said it was an owl. In the night, I'd had a mixture of feelings and I was failing, so first, I felt happy because I was experiencing camp but I also felt sad because I was missing my family. I was angry with myself for failing, but now I am confident that I can get through the night without waking up my teacher!

Romana Munnawwar Patel (9)

Queen Elizabeth's Grammar School, Blackburn

The Incredible Diary Of...

Dear Diary,
Today is 22-6-18. My baby brother, Zak, has been born. I don't know whether to be happy or sad. I won't be the baby anymore! No more getting away with everything, no more getting toys when I want them. I hope he's going to be fun...

Dear Diary,
Today is 18-12-18. I am sure I saw my brother, Zak, walking today. No one will believe me. I walked into the living room where he was supposed to be sleeping. He was most definitely standing by the sofa but, when he saw me, he fell on the floor and started to act like a normal baby!

Dear Diary,
Today is 28-4-19. I am definitely not losing my mind. I heard Zak speak today. He was speaking to someone and I'm so positive I heard him say, "Aliens." I'm going to keep a close eye on him...

Dear Diary,
Today is 11-8-19. I have something so important and fantastic to tell you. I was right all along! Not only can my baby brother speak, but he can also fly! I caught him moving his cot and, when I was about to tell Mum and Dad, he told me everything.

He is a super baby! My baby brother works for a secret organisation that protects Earth from aliens. At home, he's a normal baby, but when there's trouble, he flies into space and I cover for him at home. Nobody else knows. I am so glad he is my younger brother!

Isa Patel (9)

Queen Elizabeth's Grammar School, Blackburn

The Incredible Diary Of... My Adventurous Day

Dear Diary,

I had the most delightful sleep of my life. I slept like a baby. I woke up feeling better and the sun was shining through my designer curtains. An aroma of delicious, yummy pancakes came into my room. I jumped out of bed and quickly ran down to the kitchen to eat breakfast. The delicious pancakes were staring at me, ready to be gobbled up!

Suddenly, my caring parents said to me, "We're going to a water park." I realised why we were going to a water park, it was because it was going to be my birthday in a week!

When we arrived at the water park, we were greeted by an elephant mascot! My friend (Isha) was with me too. Happily, we went on the slipperiest, longest spiral slide ever. It was amazing! Immediately after the spiral slide, we went on the slide that had a pool at the end of it. Me and my friend were on our way to the bathroom when, suddenly, this guy grabbed us and attacked us! We had some bruises, but we were fine. This guy threw us in his black spy van. He took us to his hideout where he was going to kill us. He grabbed a knife...

Luckily, he was only polishing it. There was a bang on the door. It was the police and our parents! We were so glad. They were just in time! Our parents had found us because we have tracking devices in our backs just in case we get lost!

Ajwa Shah (9)
Queen Elizabeth's Grammar School, Blackburn

The Incredible Diary Of...
Incredible Godzilla And Me

13th March 2019

Dear Diary,

I was in my backyard. I was digging down, trying to find treasure, but suddenly, I found a Godzilla egg! I've hidden it in the basement so that the evil twins, Eve and Emily, won't kill it or send me to cosmic jail.

13th March 2026

Dear Diary,

I'm now twenty and Godzilla is no longer a secret. He was locked up. I wanted to rescue him. It was very dangerous. I went through terrifying things. After those things, I freed Godzilla and rode him to the evil twins' lair. We broke in, but the twins noticed. We battled them!

First, they went to kill us with a lorry, but we punched them as hard as we could. One of them fainted, then we were trapped. Godzilla dug to the centre of the Earth and came out under the lab. I had found a meteor in the sky. I told Godzilla to knock the meteor towards the lair. There was a huge explosion, but it didn't affect the twins. We fought for days and days until I came up with a plan to punch the meteor from the top so it would break the lair under it.

I used the super teleporter to get there. I punched down and it broke into trillions of pieces. Then we put both of the evil twins in Highbeck Prison. Godzilla then went back to his home planet, Eris.

Inshal Munir Choudhary (9)
Queen Elizabeth's Grammar School, Blackburn

The Incredible Cup Of Straws

Dear Diary,

There is a cup in my house that can do incredible things. It can fly automatically and water is in it. I thought it was a machine that scientists had made, but it came from a different planet. I don't know which one. It all started when I found it in my cupboard when I was looking for something to eat. It started to fly and I was confused when I saw it flying through the sky but, at the same time, I saw the magic straws. The straws are as powerful as steel.

The cup was flying all around the place, looking for something. I didn't know what. For some reason, it went across roads, land, streets and houses in every single country. It then went to different places like the moon, the sun, Earth, Jupiter, Uranus, Venus, Mercury, Mars and Neptune.

The cup came back, so I thought I should jump on it because I wanted to see the adventures that the cup has every day. I went up high in the sky. I saw a trampoline, so I thought I would skydive. Luckily, I fell on the trampoline and, when I landed, I looked at the cup with my binoculars and the cup saw his family at the other end of the galaxy. The cup was scared.

I wanted to help the cup to be happy and go home. Now, we're best friends. We go on an adventure every day!

Umer Aayan Khaliq (8)
Queen Elizabeth's Grammar School, Blackburn

The Incredible Diary Of... The Amazing King

Dear Diary,

I can't wait to tell you about today because I am now a king! I feel strong and powerful. I found out that I am the son of Ian and Kate, the world's best king and queen, and I am following in my father's footsteps. I can't wait to rule England!

First, I woke up as normal, knowing it was a busy day because there was a jousting tournament in a place called Paris to decide which knight would be king. I was a squire, Sir Miles' squire.

In Paris, it was so crowded with people that Sir Miles forgot his sword! His father, Sir William, demanded me to get his sword from the castle. I went to the castle but, to my horror, it was locked! I got lost and found a beautiful sword. It was odd because it said, 'Whoever lifts the sword is king' in Norwegian.

I didn't read it. In the blink of an eye, it came out! I gave it to Sir Mike. Then his father came and asked me where I'd got it from. I said, "In an anvil and stone."

I took them to the anvil and stone. Whilst I was walking, everyone bowed down to me. First, I thought they were crazy, but then I read the

Norwegian. My mouth opened in astonishment. I was knighted 'The Fearless King'. It was amazing!

Sharik Ishtiaq (10)

Queen Elizabeth's Grammar School, Blackburn

The Incredible Diary Of... Lucy And Me

Dear Diary,

I just woke up from a wonderful, crazy dream. I'm writing it down because I don't want to forget it. It was a sunny spring day and I moved to a village in Germany. My dad had bought a farm. I went to a cafe with my horse, Honey. There, I met my friend, Lucy, and she had a horse called Latte. We both went for a ride.

Suddenly, we were in the middle of a sandstorm, it felt like we would be blown away! While Honey and Latte stayed on the ground, the wind blew me and Lucy away to a different world. All around us were fields. We kept on walking and walking, then something amazing happened.

Both Lucy and I were thirsty, so we started to talk about drinks. I thought of a smoothie, she thought of lemonade. Then a door appeared and we were inside a smoothie bar! We found a smoothie and some lemonade waiting for us! We drank them and we were thirsty no more. Lucy and I were worried about Honey and Latte. After we took the last sips of our drinks, we were both back on our horses.

This is when I woke up. I felt happy it was just a dream because of the wicked sandstorm. I did feel disappointed that the smoothie wasn't real though! Don't you think that it was a funny dream?

Khadija Amer Choudrey (8)
Queen Elizabeth's Grammar School, Blackburn

The Diary Of The Queen

Dear Diary,
Today had such a horrible start. My bratty little sister, Lilly, took my alarm clock so she could wake up super early to make peanut butter, jelly and pickle sandwiches. Yes, she actually adds pickles! I had three minutes to brush my hair, get dressed, gloss and go. Today, I decided to wear a purple sweater. I was so ticked off at Lilly for swiping my alarm; I wanted to stuff her in a gigantic box and ship her off to Princess Plump and her fluffy unicorn!

"Lilly! Did you take my alarm clock!" I screamed in frustration. "If I'm late, it's all your fault!"

"I didn't take it, Mother Summer took it, she thinks you look so ugly that you shouldn't go to school," Lilly said calmly.

"Mother Summer is a glove," I shot back at her. Then I was off to school. My best friend, Chloe, came up to me and said, "Look Makenzie, a portal!" I looked curiously at the portal and decided to walk through it!

I woke up in the middle of nowhere and I could

hear people whispering, "I think she's dead, let's check her pockets for lollipops!"
"I'm not dead yet!" I said...

Saniya Khan (9)
Queen Elizabeth's Grammar School, Blackburn

The Incredible Diary Of... The Upside-Down Friends

Dear Diary,

My name is James. Do you know how it feels to break up with your very best friend? You must have at least once, haven't you? I have been through that. I broke up with my best friend Harry two months ago. Harry was being the meanest he could to me with his other group of friends. I didn't like a single one of them. I let Harry know. He just gave me a dirty look. He said, "Well, I am playing so leave me alone!" Then he carried on being mean to me!

I felt very lonely, I didn't have anyone to walk to school with. I don't like it when I feel like that. I didn't have anyone to talk to in the locker room any more. He wouldn't talk to me. I didn't like it. It went on like that for a whole month!

After a while, I decided to go to Harry's house, I felt really scared. I went to Harry's house to give him a little gift to get back together again. Believe me, it worked. He got a gift for me as well! We said sorry to each other and he told me that he'd broken up with his other friends and he felt lonely like I did. We both bought each other a game fo the Xbox and we tested them on his Xbox and became best friends again!

Rohan Gupta (7)
Queen Elizabeth's Grammar School, Blackburn

The Incredible Diary Of... Rapunzel

Dear Diary,

Guess what? Tomorrow is my birthday! I wonder what Mother will get me. Maybe some new books or a new hairbrush for my locks. Maybe one with Pascal painted on! I'm going to ask Mother as a one-off if I can go and see the lights, oh I hope she'll let me!

Sometimes, I really wonder why Mother doesn't let me out of this tower. I have given it a name, wait for it, her name is Rubyenta! Her nickname is Ruby. R and R for Ruby and Rapunzel.

Anyway, back to Mother. It can't just be because it's dangerous, there has got to be more to it than meets the eye, there has to be! Mother can be quite strict at times, so strict, I sometimes wish she wasn't alive. I wish she would let me out. I wonder if there are any other girls with hair like me or maybe it's just me...

Pascal is the only thing keeping me going these days, I don't know what I'd do without him. Life would be so different if he wasn't there. I'm not saying I don't want him, I'm just wondering.

I hope Mother lets me go to the lights. I've got to go now. I'll let you know what she says later. She's coming home at two o'clock!

Zahra Ehsan (10)
Queen Elizabeth's Grammar School, Blackburn

The Incredible Diary Of... The Day I Cheated Death

Inspired by 'Nevermoor: The Trials of Morrigan Crow' by Jessica Townsend

Dear Diary,

This has been the most confusing day of my whole life! I have always been a cursed child, destined to die on my eleventh birthday, always blamed for ridiculous things that I haven't even been involved in, always being left out and forgotten. But only two hours ago, in my dismal little house (Crow Manor), the day I dreaded most had arrived...

It all happened so quickly; one minute I was sat on my tall wooden chair, silently nibbling on my soft, roasted carrots, the next, a tall, ginger madman came charging in shouting, "Argh! Morrigan! There you are, come on, say your goodbyes quickly now. We must leave soon!"

I was just lost for words but, in the end, I trusted him. I was astounded though when he told me to jump out of my window. I mean, seriously? Eventually, I did it after five minutes of gazing into his deep blue eyes. I didn't realise where I was being taken until I saw a huge golden and white building with a large brass plate saying, *The Deucalion...*

Why am I staying here? How come I'm not dead? Did I really cheat death? I really don't know anything right now.

Maryam Bhana (11)

Queen Elizabeth's Grammar School, Blackburn

The Incredible Diary Of... A Trip To The Zoo

Dear Diary,

Today, I went to the zoo with my sister and my big brother. When we arrived, we paid. Then we parked the car in the car park and got out of the car. After that, we made our way to the animal cages. My sister was really excited, but I was even more excited!

First, we went to see the giraffes, they were so tall that I looked up at them for one minute and my neck started hurting! My brother was just gazing at them. I would have been gazing at them, but my neck was hurting too much. Secondly, we went to the lions, they had golden fur, it was so nice. We took a bit of time there.

Thirdly, we went to the tigers. After a bit, me and my sister got scared because a roaring noise came. We thought it was the lions. After that, we saw the elephants. My brother said, "They're so big!"

I said, "Look over there, it's a cub!" My sister said that the cub was cute. Finally, we saw the monkeys, they were very cheeky. They came over to us one after another. Then we went to the car park and got in the car. Then we drove home and, when we got home, we ate some food.

Eshaal Imaani Khan (8)
Queen Elizabeth's Grammar School, Blackburn

The Incredible Diary Of... A Very Grumpy Boy

Dear Diary,

I went to the park with my friends from school, but guess what happened? They started being mean to me! They said to me, "Nobody likes your games!" and that's how I became a very, very grumpy boy. This made me feel sad and lonely because I had no more friends to play with.

The next day, I went to school and nobody wanted to sit next to me or talk to me because they all thought I was a bad friend. I didn't like going to school because the kids would say mean things to me and it would hurt my feelings.

Then a very kind boy came up to me and said, "Are you okay? A lot of kids are being nasty to you."

I smiled at him and said, "I'm okay, they're just mean."

Then he shouted, "Tig! You're it! Catch me if you can!"

Now, every time I came to school, I was happy because I had a generous friend. I didn't feel sad, nor gloomy and not terrified. Soon after, everyone wanted to be my friend because I was the coolest kid in class!

Raees Khan Saghir (8)

Queen Elizabeth's Grammar School, Blackburn

The Incredible Diary Of...

8th August 2018

Dear Diary,

This has been the best day ever! It's my birthday and I got the most amazing birthday present. My mummy bought me a pet rabbit! I've named my rabbit Fluffy because she is so fluffy and white with long ears.

All my cousins came to my house to celebrate my amazing birthday. They couldn't believe that I actually have a pet rabbit. We all spent the day in the garden with Fluffy. Kyanna, my favourite cousin, put some music on in the bouncy castle. We all played pass the parcel.

Fluffy disappeared somewhere in my grandma's big garden! My other cousin joined me and Kyanna to search for Fluffy. We looked behind the garden swing, Fluffy wasn't behind there. Kyanna then spotted some ears behind the tree trunk and saw Fluffy with all my hidden presents from my family! I was so excited to see that I had so many lovely gifts like my fluffy rabbit. It was the best birthday ever! Thank you to all my friends and family, especially you Kyanna. Bring on my next birthday, oh yeah!

Dua Fatima Rizvi (7)

Queen Elizabeth's Grammar School, Blackburn

The Incredible Diary Of... The Magical Key Adventure

Dear Diary,

I'm exhausted! Me and Lyla had our first sleepover, considering we're best friends. That same day, we found a key just as we were going to eat dinner. The key had a note attached to it that said, 'Try this key'. At that moment, we giggled and didn't believe in magic. We believe in magic now!

But... where would we try and put the key? We thought and an idea popped into Lyla's head. "Your bedroom door!"

So we tried that but, here's the secret, I knew it wouldn't work. "Thanks," I heard from the distance. The door opened and, in a second, we teleported to Disneyland! There was Minnie Mouse, Mickey Mouse, Tinker Bell, Cinderella and more characters!

Once again, we teleported, but this time, we went to Wonderland! We saw fairies, butterflies and more! It was magical how we teleported. A note came from the sky saying, 'Click your fingers, one, two, three!' We were back home, just like that.

Zaibaa Rahman (10)

Queen Elizabeth's Grammar School, Blackburn

The Incredible Diary Of... Ice Boy

Dear Diary,

A school bully by the name of Cedric Cunningham had got together with his friends to attack my friends, Rodrick and Rowley at lunchtime. I feared that they would be harmed, so I panicked and covered Cedric in ice. I saved Rodrick and Rowley, but accidentally revealed my superpower to everyone that was in the playground!

There was chaos in the playground, everyone thought I was some kind of mutant! Kids were running here, there and everywhere. Some were shouting and some were screaming. From the corner of my eye, I could see a group of older boys running towards me. I started to run. I was saved by the bell... not quite.

Miss Ebrahim had seen everything from the classroom window. She took me by my hand, straight to Miss Southworth's office. Miss Southworth was silent. She didn't utter a word. She picked up the phone and rang my parents.

The next morning, the whole of Blackburn and beyond knew about what happened at school!

Sahl Musa (8)

Queen Elizabeth's Grammar School, Blackburn

The Incredible Diary Of...

Dear Diary,

Today, I went to Manchester and it took forty-five minutes. We got to Manchester and we bought a unicorn from WHSmith. We went to the dinner hall and I lost my unicorn. I started crying and someone saw me crying and asked what was wrong. I said, "I've lost my unicorn!"

She asked me where I'd lost it and I cried that I didn't know. The lady asked my mum if she knew where I'd lost it. My mum said, "No, sorry." She looked at me and I was crying so much that my face went red.

After we'd looked around for my unicorn, we went to McDonald's and I found it! I shouted. The lady looked at me, so did everybody else. It was so embarrassing! My face went red.

Dear Diary,

I woke up and my unicorn was sat on the end of my bed. My mum was in the hall waiting for me. I ran down the stairs holding my unicorn, I was so happy! I then had breakfast with my mum.

Karisma Jones (9)
Queen Elizabeth's Grammar School, Blackburn

The Incredible Diary Of... Space

Dear Diary,

My name is Matay, I am seven years old. Guess what? I won a competition to design a rocket. The prize was to go to space! There were two other winners. The day before going to space, I was so excited. The winners and I went in our own rockets and flew to space.

When we arrived, there was a hole. The two winners couldn't make it, so I told them to run and jump. They made it, but I saw a sign that said, *Mission one: try and survive the funny space aliens.* Rhydian didn't survive!

Mission two was to stay away from the boss alien because he wanted to make his army stronger. We had to jump on the planets to get to the final mission, but Yana jumped to the last planet and fell!

It was the final level. I saw this glitter around me, it was Rhydian and Yana! The final mission was a race back to Earth to get away from the deadly aliens who wanted us to join them. We all made it!

Marwan Younes (7)

Queen Elizabeth's Grammar School, Blackburn

The Incredible Diary Of... My Trip To Liverpool

Dear Diary,

My dad surprised me with tickets to watch LFC at Anfield. I thought he was joking with me, but he wasn't!

Waking up at 9am was very hard, but it was worth it as I was going to Anfield. It seemed like everyone was going to Liverpool. I saw hundreds and hundreds of coaches. Were they Liverpool fans or were they Burnley fans?

The fans had a lot of songs they kept on singing, I couldn't always tell what they were singing, but they all seemed happy. All the fans on my side were stood up and a very large man was in front of me. I had to stand on my seat and I still found it hard to see the whole team playing. Salah was on the pitch, he was amazing. He was fouled in the box! What a shame, he could have scored one at least!

I love my dad, he is amazing, the best, now I have to keep on telling him so he can get me some more LFC tickets. It was the best day ever!

Ayaan Amanjy (8)
Queen Elizabeth's Grammar School, Blackburn

The Incredible Diary Of... Ice King

Dear Diary,
Today, when I woke up, I went to check on the prisoners to see if they were still alive, which I didn't want. Unfortunately, they were, so I had to get food for them. I wanted to go to the volcano and just float around. Luckily, I'd installed a cannon, so I jumped in and shot myself to the edge of the volcano. There was another person there, so I pick-axed him to death. It turned out that he had a rocket launcher, a minigun and a scoped revolver!
After, I floated around and then I went to Tilted Towers. When I was at the top of a tower, I saw four people swapping weapons. I got my rocket launchers out and blew them up. The storm was coming in, so I went to Loot Lake. Then I saw my greatest enemy, his name was Ro-Ye-Ger.
He shot me until I was down to 5hp. Then, as quick as a flash, I spun my minigun around and he died. I got the Victory Royale!

Adam Ehsan (9)

Queen Elizabeth's Grammar School, Blackburn

The Incredible Diary About My Pet Rabbit

Dear Diary,

A few weeks ago, my pet rabbit was doing a few tricks, so she went to the fair and we entered a competition. She went through a fair hoop, she could even dance! I wondered what place she would come in the competition. She came in first place! I could put the trophy in my glass case!

My pet made a song. It was weird but it was okay. I also made a poem called Honey Bear:

There was a big bear who lived in a cave
He loved honey, but he was in a maze
He got stuck and spilt it all!

We went to the fair again and my pet rabbit did more tricks. I was so excited, but she came in third place! It was because other people were cheating. Soon after, another rabbit came from another house. They both became friends. I trained them both and soon, they were famous! They were the world champions!

Darakhsha Munnawwar Patel (8)

Queen Elizabeth's Grammar School, Blackburn

The Incredible Diary Of... Flash The Superhero, Robin The Bird And The Joker

Dear Diary,

Today, I saw Robin in the woods. I went over to him and asked him what he was doing. Robin said that he was just exploring. I asked him if he wanted to hang out and he said, "Sure."

Robin and I were trying to find our way out of the forest when, all of a sudden, Robin was gone and he was nowhere to be found, except the Joker's basement! I went down slowly, quietly and went through the Joker's backpack. I checked through all of his supplies to help get Robin out of the chair. There were some cutting pliers that I used. I chopped and chopped and chopped until I finally got Robin free! Robin said thank you to me. I said to him, "No problem." Then Robin and I ran out of the Joker's basement, out of the creepy forest and back home. Me and Robin are never going to the forest again!

Amira Wardingley (9)

Queen Elizabeth's Grammar School, Blackburn

All About My Weekend

Dear Diary,

On Saturday, I woke up and went to see the football in Accrington. Sadly, we lost two-one. After that, I went and played golf. It was really fun and I enjoyed it a lot! Then I came home and went outside. My mum got a text that said, 'Do you and Kiyham want to go out for tea with me and Erin?' My mum said, 'Yes please!'. So I had a wash and got changed and went out to have my tea. Then I went home and went to bed.

On Sunday, I got up and played football and we won eleven-two! We were playing against Lammack. Issa and Alex were on the opposite team, so I played against them. Then I came home and had lunch. I played outside. After forty minutes, I came back inside and had a wash and got changed because it was somebody's birthday. When I came back, it was very late so I went to bed.

Kiyham Mitchell (10)

Queen Elizabeth's Grammar School, Blackburn

The Incredible Diary Of...
Pokémon Life

Dear Diary,

One day, I'll be caught by a trainer. I only want to play with my friends. If I do get caught, I'll have to like the trainer. If I do like them, I'll stay out of the ball to protect them and be with them...

Dear Diary,

I was playing and trying to learn a move, but there was a shadow. Everybody ran away except me. Then a ball appeared. I used my new move and it shook the ball out of the shadow's hand. They weren't surprised I'd learned the move because they were spying on me!
I hadn't learned it very well. They decided to keep me. They forced me to get into the ball, I refused. Then they threw it at me! I was in, but they let me out. "Hi, I'm Dusk," said the trainer.
"Pikachu!" I said.
We love each other!

Iqra Aslam (8)
Queen Elizabeth's Grammar School, Blackburn

The Incredible Diary Of... The Fairy Rescue

Dear Diary,

Today, I was flying in a forest when I heard a scream. "Help!" it said again and again. I followed the sound and it got louder. Soon, I found a very tall tower. "Help!" came the voice. I flew to the tower where the sound was coming from, and shouted at the top of my voice, "Abracadabra alakazam!"

There was a small window in the tower. It turned into a small door. When I said these words, stairs also appeared. A girl opened the door and looked around. Then she went down the magical steps. She didn't see me for I was hidden in the tree branches.

When the girl was at the bottom, I found out that she was a princess! She skipped away, her dress spinning. I went back to Fairyland and had my tea, then I went to bed.

Imaan Hussain (7)

Queen Elizabeth's Grammar School, Blackburn

The Adventures Of Ging Ging

Dear Diary,

Last night, me and my friend, Nathan, went to an abandoned temple in our home country, Vietnam. Suddenly, Nathan was kidnapped by some skeleton demons and I learned that the only way to save him was to retrieve a magical katana sword!

I am now camping out in a tent near the temple and I am working out a plan on how to get the katana. I have found tools such as a bow staff and a pair of nunchuks and I think that they could really help me get the katana.

I've decided to try and retrieve it tomorrow night when the clock strikes twelve. I hope that I eventually find more tools to help me get the katana, for it is guarded very securely and it's going to be very hard managing all of this by myself. I shall continue another time...

Daniel Manuel (11)

Queen Elizabeth's Grammar School, Blackburn

The Incredible Diary Of... Aisha Mahmood And The Gossipy Friend

Dear Diary,

Yesterday, I heard Ayza Lillian gossiping about me in the talk corner and she was persuading my best friend, Zahra Karolia, to not be my friend anymore! Then I went as red as a tomato. My gossipy friend became my gossipy enemy! From that day onwards, I was a bit lonely because of Ayza.

I then had a brilliant idea to try and do the opposite of what she did. I needed to persuade Zahra to be my friend! So, I persuaded her. I said, "Zahra, can you be my friend again? It's only because Ayza Lillian is stopping you from being my friend."

She thought for a moment and said, "Of course, I would never stop being your friend!" I was as bright as the sunshine. I then told Mr Jardine about Ayza and the sun shone again!

Aisha Huda Mahmood (8)

Queen Elizabeth's Grammar School, Blackburn

The Incredible Diary Of... Man U Vs PSG

Dear Diary,

The game was tough but it was fun! We were all dribbling and shooting. PSG was really, really good. PSG took the corner and Kimpembe scored. Then I was sad and miserable. We were dribbling, we took the shot but Buffon saved it. Di María tackled me and he passed to Mbappé and he scored and it was full time.

It was the second half and Lukaku was running with the ball and he scored! After that, Mbappé passed to Verratti and scored. It was three-one to PSG. Then Rashford took the shot, but Buffon pushed the ball away. It went to Lukaku and he scored! Now it was three-two to PSG! Dalot was on the ball and he took the shot, but it was a handball!

Hasnain Babar (8)

Queen Elizabeth's Grammar School, Blackburn

The Incredible Diary Of... The Lost Scientist

Dear Diary,

I finished inventing a space machine and it took over a week to make. I set off in a hurry and reached Mars. I found an animal which was called a trylantia. Then I found a space rock, which I kept in my bag. Then I went to Mercury. It was hot, so I left in about two seconds and went back to Earth to show the others what I'd found.

The Blackburn Museum was so amazed. They took a ride and went to Mars, then they reached Mars. This time, they brought a huge rock back and it was bigger than a house! They took it to Earth and put it in the museum and everyone looks at it each day! It has my name on it and now, I am famous. They called me the king of space!

Savio Santhosh (7)
Queen Elizabeth's Grammar School, Blackburn

The Incredible Diary Of... A Day In Blackpool

Dear Diary,

Today, I went to Blackpool Pleasure Beach. I woke up and went to my mum and dad's room, then said, "Can we go to Blackpool Pleasure Beach please?"

Mum said, "Let me check the prices. Ask your dad." Then they both said yes.

We all got ready and had a small breakfast. It didn't take that long to get there. When we got there, me, my mum, dad and sister all got wristbands. Then we went on so many rides! My favourite one was the one that went upside down. It went so fast!

After all the rides, we got fish and chips and nuggets. For dessert, we had ice cream and doughnuts and then went home. It was so fun!

Mohammed Yusuf Aslam (9)

Queen Elizabeth's Grammar School, Blackburn

The Incredible Diary Of... My Dear Family

Dear Diary,

I want to write about my wonderful day. In the morning, I was so happy because I was going to the beach. I packed my stuff and put on a nice dress for the beach, but I was sad as well because my whole family (except my mum, dad, brother and sisters) were in Pakistan. I wanted to go to the beach with them all!

I have my little white cat called Kitty, she's my favourite cat. We all went to the beach and I made a sandcastle. Then, when I was making my sandcastle, everybody came up to me. I was surprised to see it was my family from Pakistan! I hugged them and we all had fun on the beach.

Hira Zafar Iqbal (10)

Queen Elizabeth's Grammar School, Blackburn

The Incredible Diary Of... The Holiday

Dear Diary,

Last week, I went on holiday with my family, it was so exciting! We went to Turkey! We were in the airport, looking for our flight. I had some Cheetos on the way, they were so nice! We went on the plane and I saw the dark night sky. It was past my bedtime and my parents let me stay up!

I got off the aeroplane, I was so tired. When I woke up the next morning, we first went into the swimming pool. The hotel that I was at was gigantic! After that, we went to the sea. I think I drank a big gulp of salty seawater. I had some food and filled up. I had a really good holiday in Turkey!

Iman Lameche (8)

Queen Elizabeth's Grammar School, Blackburn

The Incredible Diary Of... Super-Mum

Dear Diary,

My mum is amazing, she does everything for me and my sisters and I want to do something for her. She can cook and clean at the same time. I feel like my mum needs a rest because my little sister, Hadiya, wakes my mum up so much that she can't even go to sleep and I think she needs to go on a holiday. My mum has superpowers that no one else knows about. If my mum wanted to make some food, say my mum was making pizza, she would click her fingers two times and *bam!* the food would be ready! This only happens at home. My mum feels exhausted!

Anamta Shahzad (7)
Queen Elizabeth's Grammar School, Blackburn

The Incredible Diary Of... The Transformation

Dear Diary,
Today was incredible! Well, this week was incredible! It all started at school on the 11th of March 2019. I am eighteen and Bushra, in a flash, stepped on my foot! I was suddenly prettier, my world was better and Bushra was there. We both got a note that said, 'You have until the 15th of March to escape'. So we tried everything, nothing worked. We were anxious to get out. We then found a magic powder and drank it with water. Now, everything has gone back to normal but the world is still prettier and better like a dream come true!

Caitlyn McKay (10)
Queen Elizabeth's Grammar School, Blackburn

The Incredible Diary Of...Daley Okiye And The Adventures In Dubai

Dear Diary,

I've had the best two weeks of my life! Maybe there was a moment of disappointment, it happens with every holiday though. It was the area that the hotel was in, but everything else was great!

First, I want to mention our amazing trip to the LegoLand park and resort and the Burj Khalifa with lunch at the Armani Hotel on the ground floor. We had the best experience and I would do it again, maybe with a trip to Burj Al Arab this time! Now, I would also change a few other things next time, like a hotel on the beach!

Daley Okiye (11)

Queen Elizabeth's Grammar School, Blackburn

Ayesha's Diary

Dear Diary,

Yesterday, I was kidnapped by aliens and their planet was called Planet Dodo! They had chocolate fountains and chocolate ponds. First, we went and looked at the houses with banana people inside with their banana families and they were aliens. We knocked on the doors and they ran away. We saw their toothpaste in their houses. We then went to bed, the beds were made out of the fluffiest clouds!

When I woke up, I was in my bed in my house. It was just a dream!

Ayesha Raja (8)

Queen Elizabeth's Grammar School, Blackburn

The Incredible Diary Of...

Dear Diary,

Today, I had an amazing time at Flip Out. I was very happy, but a little bit scared because it was my first time going to Flip Out. Then afterwards, we went to have a party at Flip Out. We cut the cake, we had some pizza and then we had some more time to play. We all had an amazing time again! Then I came back home to write what had happened in my diary!

Eimaan Noor Qadir (9)

Queen Elizabeth's Grammar School, Blackburn

My Diary

Dear Diary,

Today was the best day of my life! First of all, we woke up and then, we had netball. We went home and I went to get my auntie, then we went to the shop and went back home to go to Blackburn. We then went back home and I got in the shower and went to bed.

Zainab Qadir (10)

Queen Elizabeth's Grammar School, Blackburn

The Incredible Diary Of... Leon And The Place Between

Inspired by 'Leon And The Place Between' by Angela McAllister

Dear Diary,

What a magical night! I loved it! Well, I went to the circus and I saw wooden toys, magic tricks and jugglers but I also saw the most special person there, Abdul Kazam! I smelt magic too, there was a magic box. Abdul Kazam, the magician, asked someone to go inside, so I volunteered and went in. I was excited and scared.

When Abdul closed the door, about two minutes passed. Then I fell onto a flying carpet. It was like I was Aladdin! Then I found a boy and a lonely rabbit. I picked the rabbit up. The boy was called by his father to go onstage. I said, "Good luck!" The boy disappeared, then I heard a voice saying, "Leon, come back to us. Leon, return!" Then I was back in the box and then I was onstage like before. When we got out of the circus, Little Mo said, "Where did you go in the box? Where did you go?" I replied, "Where magic takes you but only if you believe."

Erin Jones (9)
St James' CE Primary School, Ashton-under-Lyne

The Incredible Diary Of... Leon And The Place Between

Inspired by 'Leon And The Place Between' by Angela McAllister

Dear Diary,

What a magical show that was! On the way to the show, I thought it was going to be fake magic tricks, but I was wrong! I saw jugglers, wooden toys, magic tricks and Abdul Kazam. Before he appeared, I saw purple smoke.

Abdul asked people to go into an oblong box. No one wanted to go in, so I decided to go in. I felt brave but at the same time, scared. I fell straight down and thought my legs would be broken. Surprisingly, they were not harmed. The place I was in was unknown to me, it was The Place Between.

When I was exploring, I found an unnamed boy. He told me about this place and talked about his father and magic. Then he said, "Father is calling." A rabbit came jumping up to me. I picked it up. Before the mysterious and unnamed boy left, he talked about the rabbit and *poof!* he was gone. A few minutes later, I heard a voice. It was manly and said, "Leon, come back to us. Leon, return."

As I was holding the rabbit, I was going up into the air and I got back to the box. I opened the door and everyone clapped. Little Mo and Tom clapped the loudest. Pete asked, "Did you really disappear?"

"Of course he did," said Tom as they shuffled out into the night.

"But where did you go?" asked Little Mo.

I smiled and said, "I went to the place where magic takes you."

Little Mo asked, "Can anyone go there?"

"Yes, anyone Mo," I said, "anyone who believes."

Ahmad Lewis Abodunrin (9)
St James' CE Primary School, Ashton-under-Lyne

The Incredible Diary Of... Leon And The Place Between

Inspired by 'Leon And The Place Between' by Angela McAllister

Dear Diary,

Going to the circus magic show was so exciting! It was in the evening when we - Little Mo, Toby and me - went inside the tent.

When we saw the magic tricks, I was amazed. The wooden toys, jugglers and smoke... The smell was strong, but I was still amazed! Abdul Kazam, the magician, asked for a volunteer to go inside this magical box. I stood up because I didn't know what was going to happen. I was trembling with excitement and fear.

Before I knew it, I was falling down. I could see a carpet below me. I landed on the mat, wondering where I was. There was a boy on the mat, so I asked him where I was. He said I was in The Place Between.

As we floated around, a little white rabbit hopped onto my lap. I asked the boy what the rabbit was doing. He said that the rabbit never got called back up. Then the boy started fading away! He said to me, "My father is calling."

I faded away too and someone called, "Leon, come back to us. Leon, return." I felt myself being lifted up.

I was suddenly outside the magic box and I walked to my seat! It was the end of the magic show and the end of a big adventure. As we walked out of the circus, Little Mo asked if I really went to a place of magic. I said yes and he asked if everyone could go to a place of magic. I said, "If you believe."

Preaw Barker (8)

St James' CE Primary School, Ashton-under-Lyne

The Incredible Diary Of... The Misadventures Of Leon Sakurami

Inspired by 'Leon And The Place Between' by Angela McCallister

Dear Diary,

Wow! What an exhausting day! Do you want to know what happened today Diary? Well, it all started when me and my family went to the famous Salad Circus. It's a green circus, who would have known? It's the best one ever! Anyway, we went because there was a magic show on.

First, there were some jugglers, it was amazing how they juggled skittles. They went up and they didn't come down! Then a dim spotlight shone on a barrel organ. A million wooden toys went across the stage. There were so many, I can't remember any of them!

Next, the magician came - Abdul Kazam! He asked for someone to go into a magic box. I put my hand up. He chose me. I climbed in.

I fell down. It was like a world, not a cramped box like you would expect! I landed on a colourful magic carpet with a boy on it. He had blue pantaloons and a brown jacket on. I was confused. The boy told me that I was in The Place Between. I thought and asked myself, "Between what?" I saw a rabbit behind me. The nameless boy said that the rabbit went there every day. Later, I heard a voice say, "Leon, come back to us. Leon, return!" I felt the magic lift me off my feet. I was back in the circus! When we left, Little Mo asked me if anyone could go to The Place Between. I said, "Yes, if you believe."

Isabelle Fisher-Gould (8)
St James' CE Primary School, Ashton-under-Lyne

The Incredible Diary Of... Leon And The Magic Circus

Inspired by 'Leon And The Place Between' by Angela McAllister

Dear Diary,

What a wonderful night I had today! I went to the circus, the tickets were £10 each. It was definitely worth it and, if you don't think the same way, wait until you see it yourself. It's glorious! And, if you agree, thank you. Let me tell you what I saw.

I saw acrobats like never before, jugglers, I saw a massive amount of magnificent, enchanting wooden animals like a crocodile with really red eyes, a colourful monkey, a unicorn with a shiny horn and a beautiful tiger. I could see lots of purple smoke, then a magician called Abdul appeared.

He was amazing, his magic was like no other! Then I saw a magic box. I knew he would need a volunteer, so I stepped out and Abdul opened the door to it and shouted some magic words. I disappeared.

I was falling lower, lower and lower until I hit the ground and it was like a magic world! I was walking along, then I saw a lonely bunny. I took it in my hands. As I was picking it up, I saw a boy. He said his name was Jack, he was Abdul's son. We sat on a carpet. I didn't know why, but the carpet flew up high! He showed me around, it was amazing and then Abdul said, "Leon, come back to us, Leon return." Then I flew up and appeared again!

Oliwier Kurylo (9)
St James' CE Primary School, Ashton-under-Lyne

The Incredible Diary Of... Leon And The Place Between

Inspired by 'Leon And The Place Between' by Angela McAllister

Dear Diary,

The circus was amazing! When I was walking to the circus, I was so nervous but, at the same time, excited. I walked into the circus and it was very dark, scary and mysterious. Then the lights came on and there came jugglers, dancers, electric toys and flashing lights!

Abdul Kazam, the person who led the magic show, asked the audience if they wanted to go in the magic box and, of course, I volunteered. I regretted it a little because, when I went into the box, I had butterflies.

I fell down, down and down until I felt the floor. There was a person dressed up in black that greeted me. This place had a very tall tower and the black blue-eyed boy was sitting on a magic carpet that could fly! He told me that Abdul Kazam was his dad and, because of that, he was stuck there.

Then a dazzling light beamed above me and then, I was standing in front of the crowd, all shocked and surprised. They clapped wildly while looking at

Abdul Kazam. I didn't care though. I sat down while hugging Little Mo, a little cutie.
Walking out of the circus, Little Mo said, "Where did you go?"
I replied, "A magical place," and she smiled.

Klaudia Kleszcz (9)
St James' CE Primary School, Ashton-under-Lyne

The Incredible Diary Of... Leon And The Place Between

Inspired by 'Leon And The Place Between' by Angela McAllister

Dear Diary,

What a day! Today, I went to the circus to see a magic show. When we were going, Tom told Little Mo that there is no such thing as magic and I was about to shout, "How rude!" but Little Mo was still extremely excited to see what it would be like. Tom didn't stop telling Mo it was fake until smoke popped out of thin air and a strange, cloaked man came onto the stage.

The man did some amazing tricks and then brought out a magic box and, of course, I volunteered. When I went into the box, I was falling and falling and falling and then I landed on a carpet. It was a magic flying carpet! It slid underneath me and a boy was on the carpet.

We went into a room and there I saw the sweetest, fluffiest white bunny. The boy told me that the bunny was never called back and that almost made me tear up, but then I had to go back and the show was finished. Little Mo was amazed and

he asked me, "Can anyone go there?"
I said, "Yes, anyone who believes in magic."

Rimla Ahmed (9)

St James' CE Primary School, Ashton-under-Lyne

The Incredible Diary Of... Leon And The Place Between

Inspired by 'Leon And The Place Between' by Angela McAllister

Dear Diary,

Today was so incredible and it felt just like a dream! When I got chosen to go in the box, I suddenly felt lighter and lighter. Then, without something mysterious happening, I fell through. I thought it was a trick, but I was wrong. I felt worried and anxious. What if I fell through the weird and strange world and never came back? But, when I fell through the world, I saw a boy with pantaloons and he was holding a sparkly magic carpet.

I asked the boy, "Where am I?"

He said, "You're in The Place Between!"

I thought to myself, *what on earth is he talking about? Is he bonkers?* The boy asked me if I wanted to have a ride on the magic carpet. I said yes because I wanted to explore for a bit, so I got on the magic carpet.

I saw this lonely rabbit and I asked the boy to land. I held the bunny and I said goodbye to the boy and

I went back into the box. I leapt out of the box with the bunny!

Gracie Pinto De Andrade (8)
St James' CE Primary School, Ashton-under-Lyne

The Place Between

Inspired by 'Leon And The Place Between' by Angela McAllister

Dear Diary,

It was the worst! I went to a circus at noon near the town. I went with my sister and my brother. We went in, it was dark green on the outside of the tent. We sat on the grass. When we went in, it turned all dark and I could smell the magic! I saw wooden monkeys, birds and all sorts of things.

A man came from the smoke. He became taller and taller and, as he came forwards with a box, he asked who wanted to step into the box. Nobody volunteered but I did! He said his name was Abdul Kazam. I stepped in and I thought I'd shrunk! Abdul Kazam smiled at me.

I found a carpet. Well, I stepped on it and it was magic and then a boy found me and said hi. Then I found a lonely little rabbit. I had to go, so I said goodbye and I came out and Little Mo, me and my brother clapped. The show then finished and we all went home.

Libby Johnson (8)

St James' CE Primary School, Ashton-under-Lyne

Leon's Secret Diary

Inspired by 'Leon And The Place Between' by Angela McAllister

Dear Diary,

That was a fun evening! I went to The Place Between and it was so cool! I didn't know what to expect until I volunteered to go in a magic box and it was like a new dimension! Let me explain in a minute, but for now, let's talk about how I felt. I felt obnoxious and a bit nervous.

A man named Abdul Kazam, the magician, wore a strange mask. I went to a circus event in Pleasant Street at 12:30pm with Little Mo, Tom and Pete. When we went in, the lavender curtains slowly opened. When they opened, Abdul Kazam stood motionless on the stage.

After a few magic tricks, he asked for a volunteer and it had to be me! I stood on the stage, crawled into the magic box and I fell down twenty-five feet! I softly landed on a carpet.

Jessica Herod (8)

St James' CE Primary School, Ashton-under-Lyne

The Incredible Diary Of... Leon's Magic Adventure At The Circus

Inspired by 'Leon And The Place Between' by Angela McAllister

Dear Diary,

What an amazing day! I was at the circus and a man called Abdul Kazam asked who wanted to volunteer, so I volunteered. I was a bit scared at first, but then, I knew I could do it.

I went inside and I found myself floating in a strange place. Finally, I stopped floating in this mysterious place. Then I saw a little boy. The boy told me that this was The Place Between. The boy said that his dad was a magician.

Soon, a rabbit popped out and I held the rabbit gently and then, I heard Abdul Kazam say some magic words which were, "Leon, come back to us, Leon return." Then I found myself back at the circus. I'd brought the rabbit with me!

Klea Ballabani (8)

St James' CE Primary School, Ashton-under-Lyne

The Incredible Diary Of... Leon And The Place Between

Inspired by 'Leon And The Place Between' by Angela McAllister

Dear Diary,

What a wonderful day! I loved the circus because I saw magic tricks and wooden toys and I saw a person, Abdul Kazam, appear. I smelt smoke and there was a magic box. Abdul asked someone to be a volunteer, but then Abdul asked me! I was nervous to go in the box.

I went into the box, it took me to The Place Between. Then I saw a magic carpet and a boy. I went on the magic carpet, it was flying about the place. I saw a cute rabbit too! I had to say goodbye to the boy and the rabbit as I went out of the magic box. Then I said goodbye to Abdul Kazam.

Lennon Smith (9)

St James' CE Primary School, Ashton-under-Lyne

155

The Incredible Diary Of... Leon And The Place Between

Inspired by 'Leon And The Place Between' by Angela McAllister

Dear Diary,

Today was the most magical day because I went to a circus and there were magic tricks, wooden toys, jugglers and my favourite act - Abdul Kazam! He needed a volunteer and I was that volunteer.
I walked on the stage and went in the box. Suddenly, I fell down and a boy with blue pants caught me with a magic carpet and then a bunny rabbit hopped onto my lap. Suddenly, I heard someone say to me, "Leon, Leon," in a mysterious voice. It was Abdul Kazam and I slowly floated up, up and up and I went through the magical box!

Mohammad Sahil (9)

St James' CE Primary School, Ashton-under-Lyne

The Incredible Diary Of... Leon And The Place Between

Inspired by 'Leon And The Place Between' by Angela McAllister

Dear Diary,

What a magical show that was! I went to the circus and I met Abdul Kazam and I went into a dot. This magic guy appeared on a magical, flying carpet. When I went into the dot and met the guy, I was a little nervous because I didn't know where I was. I asked him and he said we were in The Place Between! I then met a rabbit and I stroked his fur. Suddenly, I heard Abdul Kazam's voice.

I floated back to the magic stage and I sat back down with my family and we went back home. I told my parents how good it was!

Cody Edwards (8)

St James' CE Primary School, Ashton-under-Lyne

157

The Incredible Diary Of... Leon Jonson

Inspired by 'Leon And The Place Between' by Angela McAllister

Dear Diary,

What a wonderful day at the circus! I wanted to volunteer to go on the stage. I put up my hand and went on the stage. I went in the magic box. I fell down, down and down, then it became a portal! I wondered how I was in a portal. I wished and I saw a boy. The boy was on a magic carpet. Then he asked me if I wanted to go on. I said yes.

We were on the magic carpet together, I was screaming, we kept going higher! I was freaking out. Then the boy told me about the magic!

Abi-Jo Baker (8)

St James' CE Primary School, Ashton-under-Lyne

The Incredible Diary Of... Leon And The Place Between

Inspired by 'Leon And The Place Between' by Angela McAllister

Dear Diary,

Wow! What a fantastic time at the show! I couldn't believe my eyes, I was sweating because I was nervous. I was so scared when I went into the magic box. I fell into The Place Between!
I saw a man who said he could teleport me anywhere. I thought the circus was going to be boring, but it was outstanding and wonderful, it made me feel ecstatic! Abdul said, "Leon, Leon, come back to us. Leon, Leon, return," and I came out of the box.

Ayaan Ashraf (8)
St James' CE Primary School, Ashton-under-Lyne

The Incredible Diary Of... Leon And The Place Between

Inspired by 'Leon And The Place Between' by Angela McAllister

Dear Diary,

What a wonderful magic show at the circus! It was brilliant, but there was a man called Abdul Kazam. He looked mysterious. I saw magic tricks, Abdul, wooden toys and amazing jugglers. I smelt smoke and saw wooden flying animals too!

Abdul Kazam then asked for a volunteer. He picked me! I went into the box and I fell into The Place Between...

Marwah Jhangir (9)

St James' CE Primary School, Ashton-under-Lyne

The Incredible Diary Of... Leon

Inspired by 'Leon And The Place Between' by Angela McAllister

Dear Diary,

I've found out that the circus will shut down! I don't want the circus to shut down. All the animals will be sad because they'll be lonely and the rabbit will be upset and grumpy. All the people will cry if the circus is shut down. Then the people will be sad and the rabbit won't get any food...

Sana Hussain (8)

St James' CE Primary School, Ashton-under-Lyne

The Incredible Diary Of...

Dear Diary,

Today was the craziest day of my life, but I managed to save my friends! Today, I was just heading to work and, when I got there, nobody was there. I was also late and they were always on time. *What's happened to them?* I thought. There was a sudden noise and then it was completely silent. A man said, "Why hello Daniel, it's been a long time, we haven't seen each other." Then the power cut out. The last thing I can remember was falling.

I was then in a dark room and another voice said, "Read this now." It said, 'To get your friends back, you will need to answer some questions'. The questions were very personal like where I lived and stuff. I told them my old pin that they wanted and it worked. I had nothing in it, so they got angry with me! I answered all the questions, but I lied for every single one! Then they dragged me to my friends and then chucked us out. We all got in my car and drove to my house.

Now, they're staying for the night, then they're going back home. We've changed studios as well so we are safe now!

Indy Simpson (8)

Unity Academy, Blackpool

162

The Incredible Diary Of... Ronaldo

Dear Diary,

I was supporting Lisbon today. We were going against PSG. I am the tallest from that group. João Moutinho passed to me, then I went forwards and passed to Lidneson. Seventeen minutes later, a PSG player passed to Camrea in the box. He shot and scored and celebrated like mad!

In the twentieth minute, the number twenty-eight passed to me. I shot, scored and took my t-shirt off! One minute later, I put it back on. I don't really want to tell you any more, sorry. It was a draw. I went home to watch telly and go to bed.

Dear Diary,

Today, I woke up, listened to music, had breakfast and went to practise footie.

Dear Diary,

Today, I played against Moreirense FC. We won! We were against a good team, but we won. Now, we will be against Real Betis. It will be a very tough match, but I'll chip it in the right corner and score. It'll be one-nil to my team. Then we'll be against Man United. You think we'll lose? They'll lose five-nil. I will score every single goal for my team!

Alex Ozwu (8)

Unity Academy, Blackpool

The Incredible Diary Of... An Adopted Unicorn

Dear Diary,

One lovely summer day, I was going to have my morning walk but, in the corner of my eye, I saw the most unexplainable candy cane. Then it sort of dragged me closer and closer before it touched me. I felt like I'd been hit with a bat!

I woke up feeling really dizzy, then I heard voices that I had never heard before. Then I fell asleep. The next day, I saw people trying to buy me, a baby unicorn! I felt uncomfortable about that, then I was picked up and given candyfloss. I looked at the people with eyes cuter than puppy-dog eyes as I ate the candyfloss.

A man told me about a plan for the future and a way to get me home to my friends and family. I heard him, then I thought it was a magical miracle. He opened a portal but, as I went through it, I started feeling weird, strong and powerful. He said, "No! No! No!" He grabbed me and laid me down on the floor and whispered, "You're gonna be okay, I promise." But I was delighted to find out I was actually home!

Paddy Jones (8)
Unity Academy, Blackpool

Paper Aeroplane Diary!

Dear Diary,

It was a wonderful day! This kid kept on throwing me. I was feeling the lovely, windy, warm breeze blowing past my wings. Suddenly, a mean, spotty kid knocked me into a tub of green slimy acid!

As I hit the acid, I felt fine at first, but then I got cooler, cooler, cold... I was freezing! Suddenly, I felt an explosion. Then, a split-second later, I felt warm, speedy, strong and powerful, able to go where I wanted, and I felt the elements: electricity, fire, water, gravity and space!

I tried to move myself and I could! I could move myself! I flew to the kid, Joseph, and whispered, "Hey man, I'm your super paper aeroplane!" I showed him by blasting the ground. He swore!

It was soon 12pm and I went to fight crime! I knew there was a villain on the sun so, just as the sun was coming up, I flew at 1,000mph at the sun!

I should make it in a week. I won't be hot, in fact, I'll be 27°C because I have ice powers!

Alexander Pittilla (8)

Unity Academy, Blackpool

The Incredible Diary Of... Harry Potter

Dear Diary,

Today at Hogwarts, it was really weird. First, I got out of bed as usual and had my before breakfast snack which was a Bertie Bott's Every Flavour Bean. I was a little unlucky this time because I got rotten fish! I knew it was going to be a good day because it was Easter!

I ran downstairs with joy, maybe even jumping a little. When I got downstairs, I saw that Dumbledore and the teachers had done some work. There were lots of gorgeous shades of green and beautiful blues. It was even more excellent because the shining light from outside reflected off the colours.

I might have exploded because of what we were going to do! It was a fun Easter egg hunt! First, I went to Hagrid's hut with Hermione and Ron. Hagrid had a lot of chocolate for us. We then went to the magic forest and there was a monster that had chocolate eggs for us. Then we had a happy time eating all the chocolate eggs!

Milo Duffield (7)

Unity Academy, Blackpool

The Incredible Diary Of... Neymar

Dear Diary,

Today, I started a football job. I was starting to play for PSG and I'm starting to be kind of a famous player now. I'm very excited because the manager said I'm going to play up front tomorrow! My life was really hard, but now it's changed a lot.

Dear Diary,

I started to play the match and I ran and ran and I scored! I made it! PSG was winning one-nil. I'm actually good at the game! The half-time whistle blew. We were walking out and then suddenly, a flyer hit Di Maria in the eye! The match had to be cancelled immediately!

Dear Diary,

We got to continue the match from yesterday. Why do people throw things onto the pitch? Man United were playing, so we were in trouble. Then the last whistle blew and they'd done it. They'd won the Champions League and they were cheering and raging.

Lynden Anderson (7)

Unity Academy, Blackpool

The Incredible Diary Of... Ariana Grande

Dear Diary,

One day, I got up and brushed my teeth and put on my best dress and make-up and got into a limo to Blackpool. I got up on the big black stage and a hundred million people were staring at me! I felt so nervous but I sang my favourite songs: No Tears Left To Cry and Thank U, Next. I had a very strange feeling in my tummy and everyone was cheering for me, even my boyfriend was cheering for me. My family was also cheering for me, but my dad was not there to cheer me on because he was hosting his TV show.

When I'd finished the concert, I went home and I turned on the TV and watched Slightly Less Gorgeous. It was so amazing! I rang my friends and my boyfriend. Then I went out for dinner to a restaurant called Las Iguanas. It was so cool and, when I got home, I went to bed.

Evie Sylvia Holmes (8)

Unity Academy, Blackpool

The Incredible Diary Of... Cyborg Life

Dear Diary,

Being a cyborg is great, but life is hard. My friend, Goldie, went missing a week ago. The evidence was discovered in Jelly Jungle and I'm going to find her. My life is full of stories and tales, but this one will be of Goldie.

Dear Diary,

Today was the day I went to Jelly Jungle, the pressure was really on, but no one's the boss of me! I'm fourteen, old enough for anything and everything in life.

I arrived at Jelly Jungle and Goldie's diary was left, so I read it. I read her diary and it said to eat Jelly Jungle. I did, but I turned into a gummy cyborg! She wasn't injured after all, she was a spy! I didn't give her diary back because it said that she liked me. I still don't trust her...

Lucia Panayiotis (8)

Unity Academy, Blackpool

The Incredible Diary Of... A Glue Stick

Dear Diary,

Hi, my name is Rolled Glue Stick. Every time someone uses me, my head gets smaller and smaller, it hurts my head! I just wear plastic. When someone is done with me, they should put me in this see-through box, but the fire alarm went off today, so everyone had to go outside and they had to sit on the ground.

When the fire alarm stopped, it stressed me out. I thought I was going to die at lunchtime! Everyone left me alone. I finally fell asleep. When I woke up, someone was using me, it really hurt!

When it was break time, I was thinking that I could jump out of the window or stay and hide until the holidays...

Michael John Edwin Gill (8)

Unity Academy, Blackpool

The Incredible Diary Of... Centopia's Elf, Mia

Dear Diary,

I got out of bed and my aunt brought me to a new school. I felt lively. When I got there, I saw a boy being bullied. I was fuming!

My aunt gave me a bracelet that took me to Centopia. I have four friends there called Mo, Yuko, Onchao and Lyria. Onchao is a unicorn and so was Lyria! Me, Mo and Yuko are unicorn guards.

Today, we lost Lyria. The others and I felt sad. Panthea is a unicorn murderer because he takes their horns! Mo is a prince. We noticed today that Centopia is becoming more arid and filthy. It's our responsibility to save the unicorns!

Courtney Bradley (8)
Unity Academy, Blackpool

The Incredible Diary Of... Queen Elizabeth

Dear Diary,

One day, my little child (she's a princess because she's my baby) was learning to fly. She had to practise before she could fly. Everyone loved the sweet child, but the evil witch took her. I was furious!

I calmed down and called our prince to come and help because my child was gone. We needed to save her! We got her and then we were all fine again without that witch who'd gone.

Emily Moore (7)

Unity Academy, Blackpool

The Incredible Diary Of... The Amazing Adventure

Dear Diary,

The excitement is getting too much. The day is getting closer. In another three days, we will be out there in the wild. Alone, just the three of us. We need to be brave. I haven't mentioned to the other two and I don't know that I should, but I'm feeling a bit nervous and I don't know if I can go through with it. I think it's too dangerous. What if we are attacked by bears? Anything could go wrong! I need to go...

Dear Diary,

I am back. I am getting excited because we went and bought torches, snacks, drinks and games. I am also feeling a bit nervous still because there are only two days left now.

Dear Diary,

Sorry I haven't been here because we have been packing up for the amazing adventure. It's tonight and we have only got five hours left. I am ready for the brown bears and any other attack. Do you think we're ready to go now?

Dawud Mazafar (9)
Westwood Prep School, Oldham

The Incredible Diary Of... Football On Mars

Dear Diary,

Me and Salah went to Mars on the 5th of January 2010. Two weeks before our adventure, I received a letter from Liverpool FC. This letter was an invitation from Salah and he wanted me to join him and his team to go to Mars. I was so excited and happy, this was going to be the best adventure ever!

I packed my suitcase and off we went on this incredible adventure. As soon as we landed on Mars, we saw a football-mad alien. He was playing so crazily that Salah and his team were shocked. They didn't want to lose. The alien was so good at tricks, like the dib dab. I decided to join the alien because I knew Zhoran the alien was too good! Three minutes into the game, Zhoran scored a super bicycle kick. It went flying and hit Salah, Kane and Mané and it went straight into the net! Zhoran did the loser dance at Salah.

It was half-time and the score was one-one. As we went into the second half, Zhoran's friend, Picu, scored the final goal. This was the best game ever! We all went for some fish and chips for tea and Zhoran told us how he became a footballer.

Salah promised Zhoran and his teammates that he would return to Mars and win. Zhoran laughed and off they all went. They went so quickly, it was like lightning.

Ismail Muhammad (8)
Westwood Prep School, Oldham

The Incredible Diary Of... My First Day At Westwood

Dear Diary,

First, I woke up excitedly. I was keen to get ready so I could be early for my first day of school. When I got closer to school, I felt nervous because it was a new place for me. When I was in school, I was confused about where I had to go, but I followed everyone to assembly.

Once the assembly was finished, we all went to our classrooms. I was impressed by my classroom when I first saw it. When we sat on the carpet, the teacher told us to introduce ourselves. When it was my turn to speak, I felt a little shy.

When lunchtime came, I was very hungry. I sat with my new friends, Husayn and Ismail.

It was nearly home time. I felt happy, but not shy anymore, not after I'd met my teachers and my friends! When I found out that we can take our own toys on Friday, I was surprised. I am looking forward to Friday so I can bring my own toy for show and tell and golden time!

Muhammad Adam Rahim (8)

Westwood Prep School, Oldham

The Incredible Diary Of... The Wonderful Wacky Weekend

Dear Diary,

On Saturday, I went to a bouncy castle park with my cousins. It was called Inflata Nation. It was very exciting. I could hardly wait! The first thing I did was run into the vast ball pit. One side was deep. I also went on a snowslide. First, I had to go through a tunnel, I had a rope, I had to get to the other side. I fell, so my dad took me up and I went down the small slide.

Then I played with my cousins after that. I kept jumping and falling! Then I went on the massive death drop! I was scared, but I went with my dad.

Adyan Hussain (9)
Westwood Prep School, Oldham

The Incredible Diary Of... Me And My Cousin

Dear Diary,

Me and my cousin's families went to Wales and played. We made sandcastles and picked up crabs and splashed in the water. We all walked barefoot on the squishy, soft sand.

When we arrived back at home, we all had some warm hot chocolate and we all went to sleep.

Rabeeah Noor (9)
Westwood Prep School, Oldham